THE

HIGH

ROAD

THE HIGH ROAD
The Future of American Greatness

Keith R. Kelsch

VISION IMPACT BOOKS
ST. GEORGE, UTAH
http://www.visionimpactbooks.org

Copy editing by Jeannette de Beauvoir, Copyeditor
http://www.jeannettedebeauvoir.com

Cover and interior design and layout by Stephen Tiano, Book Designer
https://stephentianobookdesign.com
stephen@stephentianobookdesign.com

To those willing to taste the waters of truth and stem the tide of a hypocritical world, now is the time of great knowledge, the kind that is not set to destroy but rather to quench the thirst of those ready to understand. This book will not help those who look to control others or to seek riches of great honor. Instead, this book will help those willing to correct our misguided thinking about American Greatness and how we should organize a free society for the future. One might think that God already knows.

—SAMUEL LOUIS DAEL

CONTENTS

Dedication and Preface

This book is dedicated to the American spirit that reminds us to stand free, defy compulsory authority, and speak our conscience in the face of overwhelming shame and criticism.

Americans have been programed over many decades to follow authority or be shamed; submit to experts or be ridiculed. From the controlled media to the racketeering of big tech; from big pharma to big government; and from the oppression of big everything, Americans have been silenced in their speech, corralled into social media gulags, and marginalized by the idolatry for authority we have allowed to rise over us. This book is dedicated to the remnant spirit within us, the open range that is tired of being intimidated into believing everything we are told.

A growing number of Americans have begun to see the difference between a leader who is compliant to secret combinations working in the shadows and a leader who defends the true creation that is our liberty. Some speak for core principles that support greater democratic consent; others hide behind the pressure of appeasement to powers they fear will retaliate against them. This book is dedicated to those who dare to take responsibility once again.

The mind that stands against an overlord class creates an automatic attraction to its spirit. This book is dedicated to that spirit. It is dedicated to the High Road that will come when more Americans choose a liberty that is a genuine rising tide that lifts all ships. This book is dedicated to the Americans that made this book happen. It is dedicated to Andy Groff and the sacrifice he made in giving his time to push for a Common Sense for our time. It is dedicated to Jeannette de Beauvoir and many like her who give bits of their soul in order to give life to another creation in words. This book is dedicated to Samuel Louis Dael for helping Atlas find his third eye. It is dedicated to the patience of my wife, Malissa, for letting me work through the years to cultivate a voice that matters. It is dedicated to the future of my children, Kaden, Kyler, Makinzie, and Parker. May your generation grab what is yours by struggle and may you build what is yours by intention. I do plan to help dig the footings when we choose to break ground.

Lastly, this book is dedicated to a liberty more like heaven than we have dared to touch, a liberty defined by people working together. This liberty is The High Road. It is our destiny and the future of American Greatness.

Keith R. Kelsch
a/k/a The Genuine Optimist

CHAPTER 1   Divided Minds

It is not about left versus right; it is about freedom versus good. The first is a deliberate division that keeps people from achieving one heart. The latter is a healthy and a productive debate, the defining quality of a thriving people.

—Debar Thomas (2021)

The Prayer

Dear God,

His name is Atlas. His education in humanity began the day he first walked into a college political science class. Like many students across the country, he found it to be a day of reckoning.

Students either become what they're taught, or they maintain their curiosity and keep their precious gift of self-discovery. Everything you are about to read is from the self-discovery of one soul. We call him Atlas, because he refused to shrug the freedom of self-discovery. It is in the spirit of Atlas that we find the will to support heaven above—even if we must do so on bruised and torn shoulders of those who have gone before us. The great test for the future of American Greatness is simple: can a young mind make it through college today with the freedom of self-discovery still intact?

If such a mind can, there is still hope for America. Let these words be some of that hope.

The "Kraproom"

The heavyset professor of political science stood at the front of the classroom looking down at a clipboard. No bell rang, but the clock told everyone that class started promptly at nine o'clock. At that exact hour, the professor stepped back from the lectern and he drew a single horizontal line on the board. It's the same line that many political science professors habitually use to show divisions in politics. It is called the left/right model.

To the right of the horizontal line, he wrote *conservative*. To the left he wrote *liberal*. He scratched a bold chalk line under the word liberal and wobbled back to the lectern as if returning from a long night at the bar.

"In this class you will find what you believe. And if I'm lucky, you will join me on the left."

On his way back to the lectern, he grabbed the American flag from off the wall and placed it in the corner behind the garbage can. He wobbled back to the lectern and began reciting a lecture that had clearly been given over and over before. He never expressed an impromptu thought; he never started the hour with a question for the class. In fact, he never looked up at the class or gave a personal introduction. He just pushed through the lecture as if he were the rear engine of a bus carrying sleepy passengers.

It was the fall of 1983, a few months after Atlas graduated high school. Spelled backward, the junior college was the "kraproom." It was a derogatory term many locals used as a label to describe a less-than-elite education that was, at the time, super-affordable.

Curved Intentions

Colleges and universities hire professors with curved intentions. It goes with the territory we call academia.

Curved intentions are often the basis of teaching civics in high school, political science in college, or indeed just about any field of study. We also see curved intentions in our media and in real politics. The common feeling is that politics will always be divisive; it will always see reality in double vision, and a curved intention is used to proclaim one person's version of the truth. A curved intention is a forced bias, not at all the same as linear thinking.

Thinking should be graspable and inclusive, but linear thinking sees in one direction only. It takes a step in that direction and concludes that, because all the steps line up, the conclusion must be true. For example, a wealthy businessman in a predominately black community endorses a conservative woman for mayor. The businessman is then called a racist by the local newspaper because the candidate he endorsed for mayor has light-color skin. Nothing needs to be true with linear thinking. It just needs to line up and fit with a prevailing narrative.

Cardboard Brown

Imagine putting a thousand-piece puzzle set together upside down! There's no view of the picture on the other side to make sure everything matches. All the pieces are cardboard-brown.

This is what linear thinking does: it puts things together to fit into a picture no-one can see.

And when we actively censor alternate views that might reveal that picture, or even a new vision, what we get is a curved intention mixed with linear thinking. The practice of cardboard-brown force-fits ideas, without anyone *knowing* the picture on the other side, while a curved intention keeps everyone from seeing anything on the other side. The cardboard-brown of linear thinking, and the deliberate suppression of ideas by curved intentions, have both taken over common sense.

For the entire semester, the professor instructed—but he never inspired. He taught that the United Nations would save humanity and that the International Court of Justice would replace the inept Supreme Court of the United States. Nobody ever debated the professor. He once dared the entire class to challenge him, but he never invited discussion.

Like a live body sinking in the ocean chained to weights that pull it down, the class was drowning in fear, and nobody dared flap an arm that might save them and allow their self-discovery to breath. Even though Atlas had been prepared—through many years of discussions with his father—he wasn't ready to battle an autocrat.

In fact, if not for grappling with his dad in many years of debates about psychology, economics, education, faith, and other issues, Atlas would have copied the professor's authoritarian ideas masked as high ideals. And after that semester, Atlas became increasingly bothered with his professor's assumption that centralized power solves all problems.

The same question kept surfacing throughout his life: why do we centralize so much authority at such great distances from the people?

Sometimes we wish we could travel back in time and challenge a few teachers and professors, and of course we wish we could thank a few of them. The words that follow are a rebuttal to a drunken academic who discouraged the sobriety of a free mind.

Like a renaissance after a long dark age, the struggle to advance humanity is not in finding effective language to communicate ideas; the challenge is having the will to express ideas that confront those in power who cling to bad ideas.

The left/right model used for teaching political science and civics to millions of American students is destructive. It doesn't help people come together. It only keeps them locked into an uninformed agreement without thought.

Of all things a civics or political science class should do, it should mainly show how people can think in different ways and still come together in self-government. The left/right political model is designed to keep people in line, to keep them in obedience to a perpetual disconnection. Over time it has metastasized into an ever-increasing centralized authority as the only solution for constant division. Since the cardboard-brown of linear thinking believes people can never work things out locally, those with curved intentions believe we can fix everything from a centralized (and even global) authority.

It may be great to have a good king or leader in central control who can fix everything, but the problem is that even the best king takes responsibility away from the people. The very thing that people hope will fix things actually robs them of the responsibility to help each other. The once-free people become apathetic, divided, and afraid to disagree. Eventually, they will suffer under the cardboard-brown of linear thinking. This same thinking imposes its will with curved intentions that claim to know the truth. The more people centralize power and authority, the more they suffer under a bent bias.

Without seeing it right away, Atlas began to realize that central authority as idealized by his professor has some big problems.

First, central authority is easily corruptible. It attracts the worst among us, and it brings out the worst in us. Second, central authority censors the best in us because it naturally favors a continual mix of curved intentions and the cardboard-brown of linear thinking. Why not call this the Low Road? The idea of common sense is nearly dead when so much power is centralized. The only way to overcome this problem is to climb out of the pit and see a greater vision. Welcome to *The High Road, the Future of American Greatness.*

The path to the High Road requires a few corrections. The first correction is a bent bias that shuts down free speech and open disagreement. Correcting for more open discussion will call for a better understanding of common sense, perhaps even a working model. Next will follow the elimination of our idolatry for authority with the three qualities of freedom that define each person and every community. Last will come a meaning of liberty that is truly a rising tide for all.

Hold your breath: we need to go under water for a bit. This is what Atlas was forced to do in order to preserve the liberty of his self-discovery.

The Study of Meaning
Critical thinking has tools and no agenda. The best tool is epistemology. The word comes from the Greek *episteme*, which means knowledge or understanding. The word epistemology came later, and it is the "study" (-*ology*) of "knowledge" (*episteme*). It is more accurate to call epistemology the study of meaning, which is the foundation for knowing.

Critical thinking is not $2 + 2 = 4$. That is logic. Logic is not critical thinking. Logic is easy. Logic is linear; it sees that things fit and add up, but not without clear meaning. Critical thinking is the creation of word equations like *faith is work,* and this is hard to help people grasp without context. Critical thinking sees that things mean what we see.

A word equation is different from a number equation. A word equation requires contextual meaning; it is more relational and less linear. Word equations need to fit and match. *Faith is work* is a contextual word equation. The use of the verb *is* in word equations means the same as the *equal* sign in a number equation. Abstract nouns use verbs to define them, and defining abstract nouns with verbs is critical thinking.

When we define faith as an action and not as a mental position, we are saying that faith is something we can see in motion. Those with curved intentions don't want us to see. They will make faith a confusing idea dependent on their learned understanding rather than allowing us to use our own eyes that see meaning in action. When we see the meaning of something working in real life, we *share*—through discussion, connection, and realization. Eventually this becomes our common sense. Those with a bent bias don't want sharing or discussion.

For example, let's say twenty students in a classroom are blindfolded to make sure there's no vision. The teacher asks the entire class to define a chair, and at the end everyone will need to agree on a definition while still blindfolded. In the dark they all speak up. They suggest words to create a definition for "chair." One student says a chair must have four legs. Another student claims a chair must have a backrest, otherwise it's a stool. More students bring up suggested requirements—chairs must be angled to fit a body, there must be glue or bolts to fit the pieces together, the seat and backrest can be made of plastic, wood, or metal. One student even suggests a chair must have a protective plastic at the bottom of each leg to keep the floor from being scratched. After some time, the class defines the word "chair" from all the contextual meanings that surfaced from their blindfolded discussion. The class finally achieves a complete consensus on a definition as part of the exercise's requirement.

The students are finally allowed to remove their blindfolds, and they open their eyes. They quickly identify and agree on an object that fits the definition. The class didn't just engage in a discussion on logic, they engaged in critical thinking. They came together to agree on a word equation that fits their context. They created a definition from that context and then found something that matched their definition. It wasn't just something in their head. It was something that exists in near-perfect agreement with their context. This is knowledge.

Critical thinking needs a relational context that people can share and see. The study of meaning is about coming to understand what something is—without being *told* what something is. Studying meaning we all can see is the only way to think critically. It is the only way to overcome the limitations of forced linear thinking that will never include your context because it decentralizes authority.

Let's come up out of the water and take another deep breath. We need to go under for another dive. Over his life, Atlas took some deep dives and almost gave up a few times. Please don't give up! A deep breath for a moment is all you need.

If *epistemology* is the study of meaning, *etymology* is the study of the history of a word's meaning. Etymology includes studying the origins of a word, its historical first use and the context of that first use. Etymology is part of the broader study of meaning, and the study of meaning in this broad context is critical thinking.

Here's an example. What does the word "apocalypse" mean? Most of us have been told "apocalypse" means a great destruction, the end of the world. For those engaged in the study of meaning, understanding the word apocalypse starts with the Greek word for "revelation," *apokaluptein.* (*Apo* meaning *un-* and *kaputien* meaning *cover.*) In Greek, the two are combined to be *apokalupsis* and then later in old French and Latin it came together as *apocalypse.* Through all this change, it still means "to uncover" or "disclose." Even if we say that an apocalypse is the "unveiling or unfolding of things not previously known," we are within the context of the original meaning.

If we ignore a word's historical context, we burn meaning. Burning a word's meaning is worse than burning books! The context of a single word, if burned, can destroy meaning in hundreds of books and articles and can even destroy entire cultures. Ignoring the historical context that made a word actually destroys history, and if we ignore history, we are doomed to repeat it.

Modern-day cancel culture is not a group of book-burning Nazis. They are worse than that. They are word-twisting, meaning-bending, liberty-destroying zealots for chaos. Their aim is to destroy context and history. Cancel culture believes everything in humanity's history is racist and bloated with white supremacy. Their curved intention is an attack on common sense.

The definition of *apocalypse* as a great *uncovering* or *disclosure of great knowledge* is the correct meaning. Epistemology uses etymology to include all relational context without any curved intention. Knowing this, the coming apocalypse is not the end of the world; it is the future of humanity that will eventually figure out a better way to organize and work together. The future of American Greatness is a big part in a great uncovering or disclosure.

Few teach epistemology these days because of so many linear narratives with curved intentions. Freud's projection theory fits here: if *believing* a thing is more valuable than is the truth of that thing, then recognizing the need to understand how it is known leads to uncomfortable contradictions. It is much easier to re-create a new meaning for a word than to seek an original meaning, so epistemology is an unknown and often avoided tool of understanding. This must change if America hopes to pass down its hard-won liberty and hopefully establish an even greater liberty.

American Greatness requires discourse supported by sound epistemology and the context of etymology. Both are needed to generate common sense on a societal level never before achieved. That may be why those interested in perpetuating human liberty will be attracted to the greater context of democracy.

Let's come out of the water and breathe in some fresh air and look at the word "democracy" with more honesty. This will not take a deep dive, just a shallow swim from now on.

The Word Democracy

Look at the word "democracy." A general definition says it is "government by the people." Other definitions say it is "a system where all the people are involved, typically by a vote," or where "each member has a right to take part." What is the difference between *taking part* and *voting*? Does taking part involve more than just voting?

The study of meaning asks questions from the relational context to clarify the full range. It does not create new meaning to fit a curved intention; instead, it finds meaning. Epistemology is the study of meaning, and it uses historical context and the time-tested use of words and phrases to remove contradictions imposed by deliberate manipulation. In the world today, meaning is changed to fit a new curved intention governed by the errors of cardboard-brown thinking.

A more popular view of democracy is an "organization or government by the people." If we can explain how people should organize, it would give us a more accurate meaning of democracy. Unfortunately, a great majority of us feel our dutiful contribution to democracy is fully satisfied merely through voting, as if voting were the definition of democracy and the only way for people to *come together*!

Is there more to democracy than just a vote? If so, what else is required of citizens to keep their democratic process from corruption? The study of meaning asks questions such as these. *What* we know becomes confused if we fail to ask *how* we know.

Democracy is a pure expression of how we know—or it should be. Thus, epistemology (how we know) compels us to see the full contextual range of meaning rather than get locked into a limited view with a curved agenda. Even better, epistemology incorporates a *working* meaning of democracy. It takes the complete historical context of the word in order to create a more solid foundation for knowing it. If horrors, such as, say, slavery or a social caste system are directly tied to whether or not such is "democracy," knowing everything about the word seems wise. If there's one thing democracy should do, it's that it should invite more context from people, and this includes the context of all human history.

If everyone has a right to take part in a democracy, are there ways for everyone to take part that we're missing? If there are missing elements in our democracy that would allow us to take part in a more effective way, shouldn't these elements be discussed and included?

The study of meaning asks questions like, "If democracy is the voice of the people, can voice be something separate from a vote, but just as important?" Well, can it?

What if the voice of the people is more than just a final vote? Could the neglected meaning of a word like "democracy" leave us vulnerable to democracy's mortal enemies, totalitarianism and mob rule? If so, then why not include the qualities of *voice* in perfect equilibrium with a *vote* to put a check on the mob? Why not include free expression, open discourse, work-through debate, face-to-face discussion, and higher demands for consent when defining the voice of the people? These are all qualities of voice that are vital to the context of democracy, but that voice needs to be connected to a vote in order to empower the people.

This is what self-discovery allowed Atlas to find for himself. It allowed him to see democracy in its greater context.

Questions come out of the water; they take in fresh air because they deliberately breathe deeply. Would not a fuller understanding of voice in democracy lift our vote to a greater level of informed consent? Is not informed consent the greater ideal of a democracy?

Studying meaning looks at every key concept and every term associated with the workings of a word like democracy. It pulls together a full understanding that explains not just what democracy is, but it includes critical action of how democracy *works*.

When a mechanic pulls a motor apart, every piece of machinery is seen as part of the whole. The mechanic sees the entire workings. A mind with curved intentions avoids discipline for words because it selects meaning from political narratives, personal bias, or hidden motive. It doesn't see the full workings of a word, its history and original context. Americans have conformed to the agendas of curved intentions indoctrinated by those in authority. We no longer know for ourselves. We are told, intimidated, or mortified into blindly accepting curved and bent meaning.

If we can all take part in democracy, and if democracy is the voice of the people, why isn't it working? Why is America dividing further? Those with bent biases feed off of the ignorance and confusion they create. They seize democracy by bastardizing the meaning of words. Like children playing King of the Hill, those in authority employ a curved intention to knock down meaning that isn't theirs.

Because of the power we give to anyone who takes control of the hill, we stop trying to express any meaning or advance any voice that challenges that authority. The game of democracy is over. The person in power remains in power and then ugly things happen—power attracts conforming minds looking for power of their own. We now have a king-of-the-hill cancel culture that is never challenged because it attracts serfs, slaves, and suck-ups who keep control over democratic self-discovery.

As division grows more perverse, there is no open challenge, no debate, and eventually no democracy. Over time people become less informed because they're intimidated by threats, shaming, and hostile anger. We may no longer have kings, but we do have cancel cultures, global agendas, and ministries of media imposed by an ever-increasing identity culture with infinite curved intentions. Like a thousand searchlights in the sky all crisscrossing each other for attention, the full moon that reflects the light of the sun for all to see is hidden behind the storm clouds of a long winter that seems never to end.

These competing searchlights are like enemies ready to shoot down anything and anyone that dares to drop below the deck of the clouds and reveal a different light showing what democracy can be. Those with the cardboard-brown of linear thinking foolishly bomb the zenith of democracy and push the consent of the people into intimidated choice.

Just because more people are given a vote doesn't mean everyone has equal influence in deciding what to vote on. A vote without freedom to challenge other votes, or to be challenged in a vote, is the missing component in democracies. Instead, we play children's games like King of The Hill because we cannot imagine a democracy with no king and no hill to claim. The time is coming when we will need to organize with more context in democracy, and more voice in our republic. The High Road is ahead.

More Context

Many constitutional experts say the United States was formed as a representative republic to avoid the mob rule of democracies and the centralized rule of aristocracies. Sadly, the mob rules the republic anyway, and aristocracies have morphed into technocracies because they've learned to control voice in order to control the vote.

A restored republic isn't what's needed (it is hard to change a society with so many curved intentions); it's easier to organize consent in how we practice democracy in our families, communities, and in our private organizations. Any good renaissance begins small, perhaps even privately.

Throughout history, humanity usually chooses greater centralized power over greater informed consent of the people. We can call this the incremental creep of control. Some people simply seek control. If there is any loophole or way to break through a democratic process to obtain more control, a nature that seeks control will find a way.

Rarely has humanity given people full consent and inclusion of voice to influence decisions. The best part of democracy is more than just a vote: it is defining meaning through conversation and consent, which together allow for the history of context to surface. Our democracy is secretly abused because those in power have found the loophole. They have figured out how they can manipulate voice in order to control the vote.

The option of increasing more voice is rarely considered by those in power because they know it is almost impossible to control voice if it is decentralized and given back to the people. This is why curved intentions used to maintain power have no need to get rid of the vote because they can control the information people get.

Liberating voice and vote by defining them in a shared context in a complete democracy has the potential to give people the most freedom. A vote alone does not necessarily guarantee more freedom.

"Democracy" is derived from *demos* (the people) plus the Latin *kratia* (power or rule.) If democracy is the "power or rule of the people," it does not explain *how* the people rule. It does not explain how people organize, how they decide, or how they vote. Without this information, we lack the greater context that explains how democracy works, and we have no single definition. We need the study of meaning to explain the democratic processes, which includes an explanation of how all people *take part* with more than a *vote*.

We're not rejecting the value of a republic as a proportional representation of the people broken into regional areas with their own autonomy. We are talking about the basic process of how we make decisions at any level, in any body—large or small—

in both private and public organizations. We are talking about how we peacefully assemble and decide something without one person, or one central body, controlling the discussion, and therefore the outcome of any vote. Democracy needs fresh air in order for our republic to breathe.

The Intimidated Vote

Let's describe a nightmare. Imagine one hundred people in a room told to select a leader. How do you think they would do it?

Well, after a bit of silence, one person is bound to speak up and say, "Let's take a vote." This is where the nightmare begins. The group jumps to a vote and a power vacuum is created when there was no need for power in the first place. The power vacuum is the immediate assumption that someone must be put in charge when nobody is in charge. However, with no leader, the universe will fill that position and give us a leader because someone stood up and created the need for a leader over us. Create the need and we have the automatic demand to fill that need.

Here's what happens. Everyone in the room begins looking at each other—and not at themselves. A quiet thought enters people's minds: "Who will be the leader?" Everyone is forced to size each other up without sharing ideas openly. Everyone is less apt to talk, and keener to hold back ideas. Each person looks to see who to align with. And those who feel they may have a shot at control begin to make allies.

When people jump to "let's take a vote," some individuals surface as favorites, and people either break into factions or fall in line. Some people go with one personality, others go with another personality. Soon one person gets the most votes. A small number might remain undecided, but they are quickly forced to take a side. Within seconds after one uninformed person says, "let's take a vote," the entire room is either divided against itself or looking to the leader for answers. Brave people with ideas are shut down, because the leadership must constantly justify its position and newfound status.

And nightmare isn't over yet! In fact, it gets worse. After all the votes are counted, a single leader is elected. Those afraid to stand on their own begin to do things that please the new leader. An "obedience" class begins to form. This new class organizes into a hierarchy that takes control of the room. Any disagreement is forced underground and muted. What remains is an authoritarian body.

No matter how benevolent the leader is, the mere existence of a central authority attracts followers rather than free and independent minds. The authority of one person in central control does not attract ideas and innovation. That one person attracts insecurity and blind worship of authority and unfounded adoration.

Here's the problem with "let's take a vote." The problem begins when the organization promotes people rather than ideas. Kingdoms of control are created, and the consent of the community morphs into the obedience of the realm.

In America this shouldn't happen, yet it regularly occurs in families and communities, as well as states, corporations, and the nation as a whole. It's now happening on a global level. When multiple leaders from several countries begin to use the same slogan, you know we have a serious problem. It is in essence the singular mistake that has so weakened American liberty.

What if we organized differently? Consider another, very different scenario:

One hundred people are put into ten groups of ten (to give more people an active voice in the decision-making). This approach slows things down; it allows everyone more time to think through issues and gives them the freedom to express ideas and opinions.

Then someone proposes that each group elect a representative by common consent and not by majority rule. Through deliberation, everyone in each small group has an equal mind in choosing a representative. The advantage is that there is no popular voting. Each person is free to disagree with the decision in their group until unanimous consent is reached. If consent is not reached, what is wrong with this? It means the discussion continues and self-discovery is still alive. If a small group cannot make a decision because one person in the group is pushing for control, then the lack of consent is an immediate check on a controlling person from getting control. Eventually the self-absorbed mind that is always looking for a loophole to get control realizes there is none to be found and will eventually give up or move on to another group to try and control.

Finally, another person comes up with the idea that after each group selects their representative by unanimous consent, a council is created where all representatives serve. The council drafts a new constitution and lists rights and responsibilities, then sends the draft back to each group to be ratified. Groups send both ratified and unratified ideas back to the council. There is a back-and-forth exchange for a period of time until the entire body achieves one-hundred-percent unanimous and informed consent. Again, if one group cannot reach consent, that isn't a problem. A quorum for the council is defined by all groups that send a representative selected by common consent.

In this new body, there's no central executive. The council operates in the same way as smaller groups, making decisions by common consent. Factions cannot grow, and those seeking power cannot sow discord. Division cannot take root because one person cannot sway the entire council and all the other groups. Those with curved intentions have no teeth to game the system. Ideas float freely and free expression is given greater liberty.

While a single leader can take fast action and appear to move people in the right direction, the risk to liberty is too great. No single person is God. The alpha-male idea that many see as the solution for "getting things done" only shuts down voice that challenges that alpha male. Using democratic consent, people are forced to become one mind—not through obedience to authority, but through informed consent. All we lack is the imagination to scale it.

When there is no political threat of shaming or any intimidating faction pressuring each person to vote a certain way, people are free to express ideas and objections. The equality of voice directs the voting; not fear, not favoritism, and no pandering. Distributed and equal participation of free expression makes voting super-informed. The new American renaissance will be based on this approach, and it will become the rebirth of common sense for millions.

Why can't one hundred people manage themselves by common consent, where ten groups of ten members in each group rise into one committee of ten? And why can't we scale this up to service regions, states, and nations?

It's because one less-informed person stands up and says, "let's take a vote." From that moment we are trapped. Allowing one hundred people to choose one leader by popular vote (51%) is worse than stupid. It's destructive. The people become divided and broken, and we call this a nightmare. It empowers the cardboard-brown of linear minds and it favors those with curved intentions. The ideas that come from this body typically have no common sense.

One thing is certain about democracy: when free speech is not kept in tandem with a vote (meaning in the same physical place and in the same group that will decide together), the average individual's vote carries no weight. Americans have lost their shared common sense because they no longer work together locally. We vote mostly along party lines where voice is limited and censored. Who actually talks to their mayor or city council representative? When we do, those in authority seem to listen only to those with influence. Our voice has no access unless our vote has weight. When everyone's voice has equal weight, the result will launch a new American renaissance. It sounds impossible, but Americans used to not fear the impossible.

Until that day comes, we must admit that we do not talk with others in our own community about ideas. We make decisions separately and alone, and we have no say in what those decisions should be. We wait for a ballot to come in the mail, and we send it back thinking we are good Americans. This is called intimidation. If you are unable to challenge the vote of others or be challenged in your own vote before you make any decision, the odds are your vote is poorly informed.

Grandma's Tree

Just after getting married, Atlas and his wife, Malissa, lived in the basement below his grandmother's double-wide trailer. Her name was Rose, and she was a noted author and religious scholar who studied Jewish history. She would eat with her eyes closed, almost as if asleep. She ate to activate her mind in the same way others run marathons to ignite creativity. She ate a lot of rice cakes and left a mess in the couch and all over the floor. She loved having company over to talk. Academics from the local college would visit, mostly to give each other accolades. One of her favorite things to talk about was the *Tree of Life*.

She would raise her hands and place them on top of her head to explain the two hemispheres. One side of her head was the feminine and the other side was the masculine. As she ate a rice cake with her eyes closed, she would explain the need to rise above the two hemispheres of the mind. She would lift her hands to the crown of her head to explain her vision of a more enlightened intelligence. She called this the Tree of Life. Her hands would quiver, and her flabby arms would shake as she reached over her head.

It is an image Atlas would never forget. It was the first instruction he'd received that a "higher mind" existed, although his grandmother's words never made much sense to him. Nonetheless, a seed had been planted, and he kept watering it.

The Tree of Life is pure opposition between two complementary hemispheres, male and female. It stands in dark contrast to the Tree of Knowledge of Good and Evil, which is a polarization of opposites that never reach agreement. The Tree of Life is two magnets turned to attract each other. The Tree of Knowledge of Good and Evil is two magnets turned to push away from each other. If you use the analogy of the two hemispheres, the Tree of Life wants to rise above and come together on the High Road. The Tree of Knowledge of Good and Evil is two sides struggling to gain control of everyone's neck.

Every deep dive into thoughtful meaning should take a High Road that brings complementary ideas together. Atlas's father had his own interpretation of the Tree of Life, arguing that "the Tree of Life is the subject, predicate, and object. When the object receives the action of the subject, and when the verb shows perfect agreement between the subject and object, this is the Tree of Life."

When Atlas's father explained the complexity of his own self-discovery to his mother, she smiled ... and, just one week later, died. Sometimes we live as long as we can until the next generation understands what we lived for and what we discovered. Atlas remembered that day. After many years of debate, his grandmother and father finally understood each other from their individual self-discovery. If American Greatness hopes to have a rebirth on a level never seen in human history, it needs to find understanding from two hemispheres; it needs to allow for a lifetime of discussion to reach informed context.

It is time in human history that we see complimentary words give context to big ideas, like *discussion* and *dialogue,* or *voice* and *vote* being complementary to something bigger, like democracy. Remember, the study of meaning is wide-spectrum context, and this is the first step to the High Road. Wide and deep context grounds the mind in responsible and working action. The result is a soundness of thought missing in politics, education, business, family, and community.

American Greatness is the force that brings two distinctively unique minds together. It does not bring all minds together; it attracts the best minds that hold the two most important beliefs. The world will soon know what these two beliefs are. First, more foundation work is needed before we can build the future of American Greatness.

A Child's Mind
Children are natural philosophers. They challenge each other with basic questions like, "How do you know?"

One child will claim "mud pies are made from dirt and water," and another child will say "mud pies are made from instant pudding." No matter who makes the first claim, one child is sure to ask the other, "How do you know?"

Critical thinking is so important to the future of American Greatness that we need to cover the study of meaning one more time—this time, from a child's perspective. A child asks questions naturally. Then something happens. As children age, they latch onto forced meanings in order to be accepted and survive in the world. They pick a side, they choose an explanation, and too often they give up the discovery process required to actually *know*. In place of knowing, we find the copied idea of another mind, which is usually either cardboard-brown or a curved intention.

From childhood we are taught agendas that fit with no picture that all can see. These agendas are forced upon us without informed consent. The natural curiosity for knowing is blown out like a candle flame in a high wind.

In America today, we have a front row seat to the dying embers of common sense. Hope rests in the vision of the High Road that we can pass on to the next generation. This vision has a lot to do with the kind of voice children have before it is burned out. For instance, children are not born with political schemes. They are taught to scheme over time. They have no curved intentions, they are natural, innocent philosophers. They ask how things work. Common sense is still alive in the very young.

In order to overcome imposed meaning with multiple curved intentions that ignore how things work, let's look at the open range of philosophy. Philosophy is like mathematics, religion, or higher education. It has many branches or schools of thought.

There are five branches of philosophy and each asks a simple question.

1. **Aesthetics** asks: what is art or beauty?
2. **Ethics** asks: what is ethical or right?
3. **Logic** asks: what is logical or reason?
4. **Metaphysics** asks: what is real or reality?
5. **Epistemology** asks: how we can know?

Teachers of philosophy tend to start with aesthetics and ignore epistemology. This allows for more personal bias to be passed off as good thinking.

Atlas's father taught the reverse. He began with epistemology and worked his way up. This is how our minds work as children. It is also how the best minds work.

For example, John Locke took the time to explain how he knows in his *Essay Concerning Human Understating*. Every great thinker does this first. They explain how they know before they share *what* they know. Children operate in the same way; they explain how they know with greater precision than what they know. Ask any child what they know and then ask them how they know it. Their precision in meaning is often astounding.

From Aristotle to Kant, thinkers explain how they know before they say what they know. It's the only way we connect the dots for ourselves. Plato ignored this discipline, and the world has paid the price for his neglect or laziness. Either way, parents and teachers are equally as guilty as Plato when they fail to teach how to know.

As children, we want to know *how things work* before we state *what things are*. Can you know *what* a thing is, like the word "aesthetics", without knowing *how* aesthetics work?

Atlas copied a quote from a class lecture. The quote said, "art is the concretization of one's value judgments." He later found that Ayn Rand was the source of this quote. Her definition explains the way art makes a value concrete. It's a concept that bothers many artists because they reject the assertion of a value judgement present in their art. In fact, some may deny the existence of a core value in their work at all, because it would reveal their curved intentions and their cardboard-brown mind with no picture. Nonetheless, we are required to ask, "What is value?"

Knowing how art is created is a huge part in knowing the motive of art, and this gets us closer to the value of art. For instance, is there a biased curved intention in a piece of art? If so, what is it? If we keep asking questions like this, we eventually discover motive. An honest artist never fears the apocalypse (disclosure) of motive because it tells how and why the art was created. When the artist hides behind deliberate obscurity and abstraction, we are left to accept the art without question.

In 1987, Andres Serrano submerged a small plastic crucifix in his own urine, took a photograph, and called it "Piss Christ." There was a foreseeable public outcry. Serrano's response was, "I had no idea *Piss Christ* would get the attention it did, since I meant neither blasphemy nor offense by it. I've been a Catholic all my life, so I am a follower of Christ."[1]

Serrano stressed deliberate ambiguity in the art, the kind of ambiguity that only the artist can explain, which he did later in his own words. "What it symbolizes is the way Christ died: the blood came out of him. So did the piss and the shit. Maybe if *Piss Christ* upsets you, it's because it gives some sense of what that

---

[1]Nunes, Andrew (February 12, 2017). "The Creator of 'Piss Christ' Photographs Trump, Torture, and a Killer Clown." Vice.com.

crucifixion actually was like." The significance of the crucifixion is much more than shit and piss. It is about redemption, sacrifice and love. Instead, the artist tells us that "I was born and raised a Catholic and I've been a Christian all my life."[2] If he is a Christian and has been all his life, why degrade the meaning of the crucifixion?

The problem with Piss Christ is that, without the artist's interpretation, the title of the work and its description of a crucifix being submerged in the artist's urine is shock value only. It communicates nothing by itself. At most, it evokes bitterness, anger, and disgust. It elicits the question, "What was in the artist's head?" Therein lies the motive of the artist, to elicit stunned reactions that bring more attention to the artist than the art. Always dig to find the motive, and you will find how and why that art came into existence.

We either hide what truly motivates us—either in abstraction or in shock value—or we willingly reveal what motivates us in the art itself. To say you are a Christian after submerging a crucifix in your own urine is a contradiction. A true "follower of Christ" would not engage in such action when it does not produce more love. American Greatness does not beget paradoxes. It solves them. American Greatness refuses to allow high-minded abstraction to hide the curved intention of the artist.

A curved intention often uses the idealism of one thing to hide the personal intention to control or demean another. People with curved intentions speak only of the ideal and not of the real intention or consequences that will inevitably surface.

-----

[2]Jones, Jonathan (April 3, 2016). "Andres Serrano on Donald Trump: I never speak ill of people who've posed for me." *The Guardian.*

A child's mind sees through feigned virtue and asks one question, "How do you know?" As the child ages, he or she begins to ask a second question, "What motivates you?" If the child maintains self-discovery, eventually he or she says, "The King has no clothes."

The moment a person answers either question, common sense hopefully kicks in and recognizes deception when the answer is a lie. If truth is still in question, we look for action to see the answer. If American Greatness is to be achieved in the future, we must look for supportive action. This gets us back to how things work.

Focus on the Workings

Stating *what* something is gives a static claim. Observing *how* something works is a revealing process. Dictionaries define *what* something is, whereas the study of meaning gives us a *working model.* This may sound like splitting hairs, when in fact it is more like splitting atoms.

You can tell an impoverished inner-city community what they want to hear, but a true leader would listen to them first. There is a difference between telling people what they want to hear and just hearing them. Listening implies asking questions. We reveal a lot more about people when we ask them questions and say nothing of our own mind. Listening, hearing, and talking with others in a community gets at the true heart and real issues. This is the atom that needs to be split rather than the hair-splitting that takes place most of the time.

We drive by homeless people all the time, but rarely do we talk with them. Some homeless people may need mental-health services, others may suffer from substance abuse, and others just need a job, a friend, or a better example of family love. You never know until you talk with them.

A true democratic process is an exercise in finding context; it reaches out to gather meaning. Those with curved intentions speak without context or meaning. They avoid it, and have purposely forgotten the child's mind that seeks to find how things work and what motivates action. As adults we can never genuinely serve one another without possessing a child's mind.

Just giving a definition about *what* something is, without first explaining *how* it works, is dangerous. Reason has workings. Love has workings. Freedom has workings. A goal has workings. Democracy has workings. Even light has workings.

Take the physics of light as an example. It has workings, and yet physicists still cannot explain *what* light is, because there is no *working* model. The definition of light has been subjected to endless curved intentions with dozens of contrived meanings. Modern physics doesn't know what light is because it doesn't know how it works. Read *The Einstein Illusion* by Samuel Louis Dael if you want to know *how* light works. You will then see *what* light is.

Curved intentions circumvent a child's natural process that wants to know how things work. American Greatness, if it hopes to have a second wind, should never give up the spirit of a child's mind.

If we can explain how democracy works without any curved intention and without any contextual exclusions, we would correct the mob rule that is fueled by hidden combinations of power organized to control the public. We might even shift our perspective of rugged individualism to a rising tide that lifts all ships.

The tide becomes apocalyptic, something individualism could never achieve on its own.

Three Dimensions

Walk outside. Look around. We live in three dimensions. Look at a physical tree. We see how tall it is. We see branches above and roots that muscle into the earth below. We call this first dimension the objective world. We can also call it "things as they are." This is the *physical world*.

Next we can look at a tree moving in the wind. Over time we see the tree lose its leaves, become dormant, and later bud new growth in the spring. We see the tree alive. We call this second dimension the predicative or living world, or "things as they move." It's the heart pumping and the wind blowing. It is pure motion and action. This is the *active world*, the world of movement.

Last, we see in our mind the significance of the tree. We intellectualize what it means to us. The tree reminds us of persistence through life and hope for the future. We call this third dimension the *subjective world*, or the definition of all things in the world, including the world of ideas, the world of meaning, and the world of explanation.

So, there we have it. Things as they are, things as they move, and the meaning of things. Atlas's dad called things as they are, "the objective," things as they move, "the predicative," and what things mean he called, "the subjective." If that's too much to put together, convert the three dimensions into trees exist, trees live, and trees are hope. The point is to see the trinity in all things. Atlas's grandmother called the three points of reality *The Word of Truth* (objective), the *Spirit of Truth* (the active), and *The Light of Truth* (Subjective). Seeing a trinity includes the live action, which is our third eye. Live action is what is missing in our two-dimensional world with two political parties and endless curved intentions. Live action shows how the two opposites work together. Live action is common sense, and we find it everywhere on the High Road.

Words like democracy, love, freedom, equality, and so on, are debated from two opposing views (objective and subjective or liberal and conservative), and never from the High Road of agreement in action. Let's admit that if we make faith purely subjective, so that it changes from person to person, this only benefits the devil who wants anything but faith. The devil's path is neither narrow nor straight; it is a prison cell for the mind. And if we say that faith is objective, as in a list of religious or fastidious practices to perform under the watchful eye of an authority, we tend toward fundamentalist behaviors—another motive of the devil.

Maybe God had the intention for us to find the High Road on our own. Maybe the "Spirit of Truth" is something we are destined to find together and not alone. Maybe faith is putting in action what we know is true. Maybe faith is not an internal state of being, or a finicky practice imposed by authorities. Maybe faith is virtue in action and not virtue signaling.

Again, this doesn't say what the action of faith is. It only says faith is action of some kind, and this makes faith invariant or unchangeable when defined in an active context. Action is the only way to show how faith works. And when see how something works, we achieve common sense.

Remember, we are Americans. We explain how things work. Any definition of faith that shows no action is a lie, because it doesn't show how faith works. Define the action of faith and we are closer to knowing how faith works. This gets us closer to what faith *is*.

Here's a challenge: Gather the complete history (or etymology) of faith, all its contextual meanings, and then collect the definitions that imply action (or how it works). Then you will know what faith is.

Look up any abstract word like love, democracy, reason, friendship or intelligence. You will find more than one meaning. In fact, you will find multiple meanings. Some history of a word's use is helpful, but modern political correctness has made etymology obsolete.

This is why epistemology (how we know) is so important. It is greater than what we know. The High Road asks how we know first, and then it can follow with what we know—always in that order. How we know gives us the working meaning because we see it in action, and this is common sense.

Dad's Brain

Walking home from school every day, Atlas was always pleased to see the familiar silver pickup parked in the driveway. It meant Atlas's dad was home.

School ended at 2:40, and Atlas's dad made sure he was home at the right time to talk with his five kids. He managed the advertising department at the News Chronicle, a local newspaper in Thousand Oaks, California. His name was Samuel, and he always took a late lunch so he could write about physics and talk with his kids.

Back in those days, in the early 1980s, Samuel used a Radio Shack computer to write. He saved his writing digitally on a reel-to-reel tape recorder because the computer didn't have enough memory to save everything. This was years before floppy drives— and decades before the USB drive and later the cloud.

His first book argued for a unified field theory in physics, something Einstein had never figured out. He wrote under a pen name because he feared nobody would listen to a physics theory shared by a common advertising salesperson. The obscurity of the pen name, he hoped, would put the attention on his theory instead of his lack of status.

Atlas's father didn't use the scientific method to figure out the physics of light. The scientific method involved too many assumptions; it's made observation purely objective and factual. It begins with formulating a hypothesis through induction based on observation. Then experiments are employed to test the deductions drawn from the hypothesis.

Samuel had a problem with induction from observation. It was, he thought, like making a guess, testing that guess, and making conclusions derived from observation—which is more guessing. That's the scientific method. It concludes that observation is fact, or objective.

In truth, observation is active, and not objective. Observation is the third eye to show agreement. It is not a fact you hold in your hand. It is the action that shows agreement—it is seeing the definition of a chair agree with an actual chair. The scientific method has become a conclusion from a two-dimensional view with no third eye to show agreement. In other words, the scientific method lacks a three-dimensional relationship.

Samuel's method employed more epistemology than a guessing and testing process. He even gave this method a name: the *predicate reality*, governed by something he called *the law of invariance*. The predicate reality and the law of invariance give a disciplined approach to securing knowledge. Together they keep us from falling to curved intentions or cardboard conclusions. This disciplined approach demands a three-dimensional method for knowing.

He later wrote a second book called the *Platonic Idiom* wherein he spelled out how he knows anything in detail. If you want to know more, read the book. Like all enlightenments in the past that achieved great things, a few philosophers always spoke first as a foundation for a new and better world.

It Takes Three

After arriving home from school, the A-kids (Adam, Atlas, Annie, Aria, and Andy), would find their dad napping on the couch. He used a short nap to dump paradoxes into his sub-conscious. The afternoon rest helped him figure things out, a practice all the best minds use. While the brain works hard when awake, sleep allows the subconscious to process paradoxes. When the mind awakens, it is fresh. Samuel would come back to the computer with new clarity that would get him closer to the true meaning of space, time, and the workings of light. The A kids never bothered their dad during his afternoon nap because it meant he was working.

Before Atlas's family moved to California in 1979, his father attended the University of Utah where he took a freshman writing class. The professor taught that every sentence must have a subject, predicate, and object, and that this makes for a complete thought. This stuck in Samuel's mind for the rest of his life and became the foundation for his epistemology and eventually his unified field theory.

During the move to California in the summer of 1979, the family pulled over and let their dad sleep in the cab of the U-Haul while the kids jumped back and forth across the Arizona/Nevada border. Something happened during the move to Los Angeles, and it was more than a change in music from disco to punk rock. It was the beginning of a mini-renaissance within one family. A college dropout who became an advertising salesman moved to California with his wife and five kids ... and he was going to create a unified field theory in physics.

We can only hope that some value in our lives will eventually make impact. All lives are meant to have impact, not just the lives of those who attended the right schools, became rock stars, or toed the line.

As Samuel worked during his lunch hour through paradoxes in modern physics, he would place words in their proper and invariant places.

A rock is a thing, and the word rock is the equivalent in language to that thing. A rock tumbling through a river shows the existence of the rock, its breakdown, and its active lifecycle. Concrete words are easy to place in the objective or physical world. These types of nouns are things as they are. Abstract words are more difficult to place. They are something in live action. Words like liberty are invariant (unchangeable) in an active reality. They are not subjective interpretations, and they are not constricted to objective things. They are best known in the middle action between objects and subjects.

In other words, the action of the verb explains how things work.

Explain the action of liberty and you will know its true meaning. Explain the workings of friendship and you understanding how to be a friend. Common sense sees the meaning of words in live action. We call the action of the verb something in motion. Love, liberty, and even lust show action. A rock, however, does not need to show motion to reveal its meaning. A rock communicates itself perfectly as a static object.

Freedom, on the other hand, is not a static object. It is an abstract noun, and abstract nouns are best known in motion as they interact. Common sense sees that motion. Any time a complex word is used in writing or speech, look at how it behaves in action. The action reveals the best meaning. For example, consider two definitions of love.

1. Love is friendship caught fire.
2. Love is letting go of fear.

The action of "letting go" reveals more meaning about love than using *friendship* and *fire* to claim what love is. If love is friendship caught fire, we are still left trying to figure out friendship, another abstract noun. Even when one abstract noun like *friendship* is used to define another abstract noun like love, we still cannot see love in action, or understand how it works. "Letting go of fear" shows a meaning we all can see and actively experience. Focusing on understanding the action of "letting go of fear," we can resolve any contradictions and understand its meaning with no confusion.

This is called common sense. It is nearly impossible to argue against common sense. Those with curved intentions struggle to twist meaning where anyone can see a meaning that is working just fine.

Common sense takes the meaning that expresses more responsible action, not the meaning with static inaction that leaves the mind still wanting to see something in motion.

Seeing the action of responsible and live motion in complex words is the backbone of common sense, a skill we have been intimidated into forgetting due to the rise of political correctness and the wokeness culture of identity politics. Cancel culture has one mission: to erase common sense and replace it with a moving target and no vision.

Not every generation represents an automatic improvement on prior generations. Sometimes we get stuck and we lose our third eye.

Following the Action of Light

Samuel was born in 1939, in a generation that still asked how things work. He would not ask what light is. He would ask how light works. Because he started asking how, he focused on the action to explain the truth.

Before Einstein, Michael Faraday in the 1800s thought that both the electric field and the magnetic field have some type of particle nature. He performed experiments to see how the electric field and the magnetic field act in relation to each other. Observation concluded that the two fields act at right angles to each other. Faraday created equations that are to this day still accepted. The problem is not with the equations but with Faraday's assumption that light travels at a constant velocity everywhere throughout the universe. This was based on his idea that both the electric and magnetic fields have no particle nature to affect the speed of light.

Samuel wasn't a mathematician, but he thought the right-angle observation was missing because of Faraday's assumption that light travels the same everywhere in a straight line and through all matter. He concluded that if there is a right-angle relationship, then something exists that causes it to happen. Modern physics generally teaches that light has a linear relationship, from point to point, and that it maintains this constant straight direction through all space and through all magnetic fields with no alteration. This doesn't agree with the right-angle relationship we perceive through observation.

Even if there are no magnetic particles, there is a force between magnetic and electric fields that affects light, causing it to bend and maybe slow down. The only way this can be explained is the right-angle relationship. For example, as light passes a planet in space, it curves or bends into that planet because of its magnetic density. The workings of light are not linear, but angular. In other words, light is an electric spiral around a magnetic field at rest. If you add some type of density to the magnetic field, you must conclude that light does not travel at a constant velocity through that density.

Imagine a satellite traveling at right angles across the night sky. If you keep the orbital momentum just right, the satellite curves around the earth, never to fall into the earth and never to escape the earth's magnetic field. This is a right-angle relationship. If this was not true, the earth would fall into the sun. It is the interaction of the magnetic field in space and the electric particles moving at a specified velocity or momentum that explain the workings of light. Once something loses or gains momentum as it moves, it either falls into planetary bodies or it escapes into space. Light is no exception.

Light doesn't travel in a straight line from its original source. The velocity of light is determined by the magnetic density it travels through. It's like sitting in a canoe and dipping your paddle in the water as your partner rows. The canoe begins to turn in the same direction as the paddle in the water. Light behaves the same way. To know how light operates is a big clue in knowing what light is.

Let's apply this to atomic clocks. While one clock seems to slow down in a denser magnetic field at sea level, another apparently speeds up in a less dense magnetic field on top of a mountain. After a period, they can be brought back together to consider the difference in time. Time doesn't slow down; it's the variable density of the magnetic field that affects the clock. In other words, the magnetic field is like the pressure at great depths in the ocean. Drop a watch in the ocean and eventually, at the right depth, the pressure will stop the watch from working. This doesn't stop time; it stops the watch. If we conclude that time is relative (it changes) to fit our need to rewrite the universe with curved intentions, we will ignore the truth.

Why mention all this about the physics of light? Because American Greatness refuses to accept a paradox. It demands to know the true workings. A variable magnetic density around the earth explains the workings of light. It's like having your ears pop as you drive up the mountain, the change in atmospheric pressure has an effect on your ears. In like manner, it should be taught that a time piece is equally affected in a denser magnetic field at sea level than the lesser dense magnetic field on top of a mountain.

Place a watch on the surface of the moon and it will measure time differently than on the surface of earth or the sun. Does this stop time? Obviously not. However, if the mind wants a bug-eyed universe filled with curved intentions and paradoxes to manage their own need to control reality, it will ignore the workings, fabricate a new theory, and deny common sense. Atlas never understood this until one early morning cleaning garages with his father in Los Angeles. It was a part-time job to bring in extra money for the family as well as a time to think before the world woke up.

Dust in the Medium

Atlas's father nudged him out of a deep sleep. "Atlas, get up, I need help with the garages."

Groggily, Atlas crawled out of bed and dressed himself in leftover jeans, a dirty t-shirt, and some old Converse shoes, and bumped down the hall in the dark to exit the house.

His father sat waiting in a truck with a huge vacuum system attached to the undercarriage. Atlas stepped in and quickly regained his reverie leaning against the car door. Strands of blond hair caught wind through a crack in the window as his father drove to Los Angeles. A late-night talk radio program in the background debated over the validity of a singularity as a cosmological first origin for all things.

"If everything originated from a single physical point not any bigger than the tip of a pencil, what existed outside that singular point?"

"Nothing."

"Not even space?"

"Correct, nothing. ..."

"You know how incomprehensible that sounds."

"This is the truth of our multiple-dimensional reality."

It took about forty-five minutes for Atlas's father to arrive in downtown Los Angeles, and they'd left a good hour before the polluted sunrise turned into a dirty, soiled brown, much like a rotten orange with a light bulb inside it.

At the top of a parking structure, Samuel was sitting in near quiet for a moment waiting for Atlas to finish up is work blowing garbage into a center line to vacuum up. Considering the city in the shadows of the early morning light, he asked Atlas, "What do they do in these buildings all day?"

"I don't know," replied Atlas.

"They push papers and speculate. They don't produce anything, and they don't create anything. They speculate."

Without any thought about how to respond, Atlas stepped out and, in a few minutes, refueled the blowers with a gas can as his father took a short fifteen-minute nap. The talk radio program continued the discussion.

"So, you're saying UFOs are products of black operations by our own government?"

"Yes."

"And one day they will roll these UFOs out as a massive interstellar threat that will unite the world under one global military force that will empower a super technological elite."

"Yes, that is the plan. ..."

Atlas sat on the warm hood of the truck and listened. He never could wake his father, so he just sat until Samuel woke naturally. Samuel needed any sleep he could get, working as a managing ad director by day and a garage janitor by night, and Atlas used this time to be awake about what he saw and heard, which was nothing but a mass of sticky images and impressions—to the untrained mind.

He sat there thinking about the importance of a dream and yet at the same time the fatalistic notion of having a goal without a dream to organize one's life. Dreams and goals are not the same thing, and yet what is one without the other? The answer was asleep. It was his father, a man full of vision and yet with no direction, at least none that Atlas could see. Atlas had no language to express this concern, but he did feel it. In fact, he was beginning to feel too much.

A morning breeze kicked up and Atlas turned around on the hood to see his father writing on a pad of legal paper under the yellow glow of the dome light. Atlas slid off the hood and got inside.

"Is light a particle, or a wave?" his father asked.

"I don't know."

"It's neither," said his father. "It's a spiral helix ... Don't ever get stuck between two positions, there's always the predicate."

"Dad, all through high school you've said that word, predicate, over and over. What does it mean?"

"It's the responsibility of a live axiom."

"And what does that mean?"

"Just that: it's the action of responsibility." Sensing confusion in Atlas's eyes, his father grabbed a small piece of string from his tattered jacket and tied one end to the stick shift and the other to the steering wheel.

He took his dull pencil and pretended to walk his fingers across the stretched-out string. "The predicate is like a tightrope walker reaching out to the left and to the right with a very long pole. The pole is heavy, an inch thick, and weighs about twenty pounds. Now imagine along this pole you find the subjectivists to the left, and to the right you find the objectivists. Each serves only a position in thought, whereas the predicate is a third position of thought referencing the others at the same time, and yet it can exist on its own."

"I don't understand."

"The predicate is not the pole, but the grabbing of the pole. Think of it as you would think of love or harmony. None of them would exist without a sense of equilibrium. When the tightrope walker begins to fall to the right, he grabs the pole and rights himself. When he falls to the left, he grabs the pole again to regain balance. Without the pole to grab, he would fall."

"Yes, but why the word predicate? What does predicate mean?"

"It's more of a philosophy than a single meaning for a word. The predicate is grabbing the pole, which is why the predicate is a philosophy of action."

Moments passed without a word. Not many use the word philosophy with as much comfort as Atlas's father. It came out of his mouth with the same comfort as the word *apple*.

"... Yes, that's it, the predicate is a philosophy of action and responsibility rather than taking a position ..."

At that moment the sun crested the horizon and revealed thousands of dust particles floating in the cab of the truck. Like wisdom upon first expression, the phrase "taking a position" quickly fell into incomprehensibility as fast as the night stars behind the crack of the sun. Atlas's father drew his attention to the light coming through the window and said,

"Existence cannot have a singularity. It takes two things in opposition to bring about a third element, and yet only when two elements have things in common do you have singularity, which is meaning. Meaning is singular; existence is opposition in all things. They—" referring to those on the radio—"are looking for a singularity in existence but not a singularity in meaning, and that is the mistake of modern physics; they have no epistemology. They fell off the tightrope."

Atlas later in life concluded that we've become intoxicated with creating new theories completely foreign to common sense.

A new theory can assume time is malleable, like the atomic clock itself. If we want this kind of confusion, we'll continue in the dark. If we don't, we must take the High Road. We must improve our critical thinking to include the predicate. We must demand answers that explain how things work. We must have a pole to grab. Atlas was beginning to think like his father on his own accord, and with his own self-discovery. He just lacked his own voice.

Over time we've given too much power to authority and we've allowed abstract explanations and academic obfuscation to take hold without explaining how things work. Ask anyone how democracy works, and you'll hear countless arguments about what democracy is. But you will not hear how it *works*.

We have given the *power of the people* to authorities and elitists with curved intentions. Artists are telling us what art is without revealing their motives. Many scientists are curve-fitting what they observe around biased theories, and politicians are manipulating the democratic process to maintain power. We have lost common sense. It is time to engineer the study of meaning better. It's time for America to finally see through the curved intentions that employ the cardboard-brown of linear thinking which is falsely called diversity.

The Predicate Reality

The best meaning for what something is can be found in the action that explains *how that something works*. Abstract words like "democracy" or "light" can typically scare a lot of people because they fail to see a working model and they get caught up in their speculative complexity. We then default to authority to tell us what something is, and we subject ourselves to their conclusions with no freedom to question.

Bring up important words that matter, like the word "liberty," and it can spook a mind. If that mind has not exercised thought about how each word works, it will tend to shun or shame a mind that has exercised its own self-discovery.

Common sense tells us how things work. Self-discovery lets us see that on our own.

In any dictionary, we find both concrete and abstract nouns. What we tend to ignore is that many English nouns can be verbed, meaning they can be used as a verb, though some are more resistant than others. Look below at the two lists of words. While some of the words on the left can be converted to a verb, as in "Shakespeare *penned* Hamlet," the words to the right cannot be defined as static objects like those to the left. It is not enough to label the list on the left "concrete nouns" and the list on the right "abstract nouns." There is more.

Pen	Freedom
Bat	Democracy
Dirt	Equality
Oxygen	Learning
Hardhat	Light
Grass	Friendship
Peanut	Government

Language is based on three concepts, not two. We can communicate with two, but we make greater meaning with three. Atlas's dad called the third concept the predicate reality. His grandmother called it The Tree of Life.

Atlas needed to find his own way.

The predicate reality is the inclusion of a third eye. The best way to describe this third eye is to imagine seeing around a telephone pole. One person can see only one side of the pole. Another person on the opposite side of the pole sees only the opposite side of the pole. Neither person sees all the way around the pole. It takes a third person to *walk between* and see the two sides together in a way no single person can see.

The *action between* is the predicate. It is a reality of action and responsibility rather than taking a static mental position. This is how common-sense works; it walks between and sees what no single view can see. It takes responsibility. It takes action to see and this action walks between.

Common Sense Reborn

A great number of Americans used to say, "Wait a minute, let me see." We used to demand to see for ourselves. We would "walk between" to see what each of two sides are not seeing. This is called observation. Observation is the act of seeing agreement between the subject (the definition) and the object (things). It is not the conclusion from the observation. It is the observation itself, which is the act of seeing, measuring, and testing for agreement.

Common sense needs three things in order to be reborn at a level we haven't yet seen. It needs a *definition*, it needs the *physical world* to receive that definition, and it needs to *observe* action between the physical and the definition to show agreement.

Ideas are definitions. Facts are things. Observation sees the definition of something in action or that is acted upon.

When we have a definition of a chair in our head and when we observe a physical object that agrees with that definition, this is the very definition of knowledge.

Sophisticated scholars will debate this and come up with confusion and more bafflement to glorify their own intelligence.

Meanwhile, common sense is the observation that verifies the definition, it is not fact and it is not the chair itself. It is seeing a definition *match* an action or thing in the physical world.

This is how Atlas's dad corrected the scientific method. He refused to make observation fact. He made observation our third eye.

Over time his dad's epistemology gave better insight into economics, religion, and so much more, because it recognized the action that shows the definition best. Rather than resorting to highbrow thinking that focuses on what things are, with an infinite regression into hair-splitting debates, it's time to focus on how things work. Common sense is based on how things work.

For Atlas, a commonsense rebirth didn't come until after years of feeling stuck in the duality of left/right thinking. He couldn't find how democracy worked using his father's subjective, objective, and predicative model. And his grandmother's Tree of Life didn't quite clarify it for him either. Atlas needed his own third eye to separate the forest from the trees. He needed to exercise his own self-discovery. He needed a trinity of meaning closer to the workings of common sense. He needed a trinity that would explain the workings of democracy. He found this when he discovered three qualities that validate the freedom of each human being. Once he found these qualities, he discovered the High Road and the future of American Greatness.

It didn't happen by accident. It came through a persistent internal debate and the hidden encouragement of providence.

CHAPTER 2 The Trinity

Were my soul trembling on the wing of eternity, were this hand freezing to death, were my voice choking with the last struggle, I would still, with the last gasp of that voice, implore you to remember the truth: God has given America to be free.

—Patrick Henry (1736–1799)

The Fence

In a desert community in the southwest corner of Utah, Atlas was trying to drive a campaign sign into the ground.

It took several attempts to penetrate the hard dirt. Some homes in the subdivision had horses standing in their backyards, motionless, as if drugged. Brittle tumbleweeds were piled in corners from high winds. It was mid-October, near the end of a dry summer, and it was campaign season, roughly thirty-five years after Atlas first realized he needed his own third eye. He was about to find it. By this time he was married with three grown children, and for some reason he decided to run for office.

Several "no trespassing" signs decorated a six-foot chain-link fence. A padlock on the gate made sure the owner would manually open it every time he came and went. Inside the fence, two overfed chocolate labs ran back and forth on a compacted dirt path that swirled around dried sagebrush and desert cacti.

The owner kept his face hidden under a dirty baseball cap as he walked up to his fence and squinted at Atlas. The man's unshaven face looked as if he'd been in seclusion for several weeks.

Atlas had just placed a sign into the stiff volcanic ground, about thirty feet from the man's property, which was the first one on the left as you entered the subdivision. It may have been the noise of the sledgehammer against the metal that had disturbed him, but Atlas sensed something else bothered the man.

"I'm running for House District 75," Atlas told him.

"What party." The man made it into a statement.

"Independent American," Atlas answered, reaching to hand him a flier.

"No, thanks. I vote strictly Republican," he grumbled.

The unhappy man turned abruptly to walk back to his house. With his back to Atlas, he mumbled under his breath—but still loud enough for Atlas to hear—"I'm voting straight red this year."

A faded American flag flapped in the wind against a galvanized flagpole just two feet from his home. The man remained locked away from his community even while professing patriotism for his country. Unlike Robert Frost's famous line, "good fences make good neighbors," this situation was more like "locked gates discourage good neighbors." Two men in the same community who very much needed to talk were separated by a fence.

After several encounters with similarly self-quarantined citizens, it became clear to Atlas that we run into ideas before we run into people. More to the point, we run into our *own* ideas before we run into people. Some call this typecasting. Others call it cognitive dissonance. A better description is *uninformed apprehension*.

We put up preconceived ideas about people (a padlock) before we genuinely meet them. Self-isolation is the canary in the coal mine when it comes to forecasting a collapsing culture.

Every day around the world people are discriminated against because they are independent thinkers. They express an independence of mind that naturally threatens those in power or those locked inside iron bubbles of thought. These apprehensive minds protect what they've built, usually judging new ideas and innovations as tricks meant to steal their precious control. Instead of willingly sharing authority and inviting community collaboration, they dominate the community with their need for control.

Imagine running a business, and Martin Luther King Jr. submits an application for a public-relations position with your company. Would you hire him? Most people wouldn't, because they don't know how to manage leaders greater than themselves. Imagine receiving an application from George Washington to be a surveyor in your land-development company, or Shakespeare to be a technical writer for your marketing business, or the economist Adam Smith to help with designing a curriculum for an economics degree. Would you hire any of them? It's doubtful. They would threaten your control.

Discrimination against a person's real ability happens all the time. It has little to do with gender, race, personal identity, or group affiliation; it has everything to do with control. This kind of discrimination against a person's real ability is the worst there is, and it's far more disturbing and pervasive in American organizations than we realize. It's the kind of discrimination used if you want to shut people down and control them. All you have to do is favor some minority class, or a special-identity group, and you can censor the political, philosophical, and ideological views of anyone you dislike—*including* those in the minority and special-identity groups. It is the cheapest trick in the book. Hiring a gay Jewish woke male who identifies with cancel culture aggression allows you to *not* hire a gay Jewish libertarian who has a fiercely independent mind.

Nations are ready to collapse when power attracts the most controlling who debase others to protect their authority. Call others who challenge your authority racists and you can excuse yourself from being questioned.

Discrimination against a person's work in life happens because it threatens established power. Discrimination of this type is worse than all other types of discrimination, because it is against human creation, the purest expression of human agency. When a person places stumbling blocks in the way of another person's creation, humanity is twice cursed. The obstruction doesn't harm only the person who created that value, it harms everyone who might benefit from it.

Thomas Jefferson started the *Declaration of Independence* with "We hold these truths ..." What do Americans hold in common today? If there is one question that Atlas had in his mind after all these years, it was this. What will bring people back to *we hold* without uninformed apprehension getting in the way? Americans must answer this question. And we must answer it in the face of an active opposition that wants Americans to hold nothing in common except obedience to more control.

A great community is not a group of people categorized by gender, race, religion, political party, or group identity. A great community exists without any identifiers and recognizes the trinity in each person's conscience (their voice), each person's consent (their vote), and each person's creation (their value). It's time for Americans to come together under a trinity we can all see. The true uniqueness of people in a community is in the pure context in meaning they create together, which can only happen through the greatest consent possible. Understanding this is the antidote to uninformed apprehension. If you haven't noticed, you have just been given the trinity that Atlas had been looking for all his life.

The Box

We're told to think outside the box, but this is deceptive because we still need to get *inside* the box where all the decisions are made. What America needs is not out-of-the-box thinkers. We have enough of those. America needs greater access inside the box. So why not create a new box to accommodate more involvement? As long as we have the liberty to peacefully assemble as private citizens, we are free to organize. The United States was one of the first countries to establish the right to peacefully assemble. It was so important that it became the new nation's first amendment to its constitution.

> Congress shall make no law respecting an establishment of religion, or prohibiting the free exercise thereof; or abridging the freedom of speech, or of the press; or the right of the people peaceably to assemble, and to petition the Government for a redress of grievances.

The right of the people to *peaceably assemble* is the only right that requires more than one individual. You can *speak* alone, but you cannot *assemble* alone. The right to peaceful assembly is the right to experiment in self-government.

After the experience of running for a state legislative office, Atlas had a clear and compelling thought: America needs to reawaken its experiment in self-government. The up-close look into the workings of running for office led him to believe that America needs a better way for people to come together. Good people are willing to serve and add value, but their voices are filtered, censored, and kept from expression because of the uninformed apprehension created by a bent bias. Remember, a mind with a curved intention will silence alternative views because it already "has" the truth. A curved intention is a derailment of counter arguments before they are given a chance to find expression.

When people reject the idea of a king, executive, or defaming philosophy that eliminates threats to those in control, and when people choose instead wide consensus, it is called a *new beginning*. New beginnings happen the moment people abandon their idolatry for some central authority.

New beginnings are not revolutions; they are fresh starts. In a revolution, we overturn existing power. In a fresh start, we peacefully assemble for a common good not controlled by the established power. If the established power fights against a peaceful assembly, it *is* the cause of the revolution, not those who peacefully assemble. This is how the United States was born. It began as a fresh start. The original founders didn't start the fight. They did not even exercise civil disobedience. They started a renaissance.

It may be hard to believe that people can peacefully assemble to organize a fresh start and ignite a renaissance in human liberty. But people can peacefully assemble, even though such an act stands against the bent bias of those in power.

When in the course of human events, it becomes necessary for one people to dissolve the political bands which
have connected them ... they should declare the causes
which impel them to the separation.

Americans have lost the art of peacefully assembling because
they have forgotten the fuel that feeds liberty. That fuel is *voice.*
For more than one hundred years, we have given our voice to vertically integrated hierarchies. During this time we have groveled
to that hierarchy. We now fear retaliation if we suggest common
sense. A fresh start can bring us closer to each other if we choose
to see people and their ideas in the open, where no party, power,
or defaming authority can intimidate or censor us. Censorship
isn't fuel, it is a wet towel over a dying fire. Any hope for liberty
needs to get out from under the wet towel and breath again. A
fresh start begins with voice.

V Is For Voice

The ability to talk and share ideas without barriers is central to
a fresh start. We call this voice, something different from a vote,
but equally important.

For too long we have lost our voice. Voice is the single greatest function that validates individual freedom—while at the
same time defining a free society. Let's unearth the dynamics
of voice, because without it we're left with yet more uninformed
apprehension and the curved-discrimination that goes with it.

For starters, voice is your mind. Voice is your intelligence
and the education you have worked to obtain, hopefully unencumbered by curved intentions. Voice is the unique experience

you have lived, your ideas, vision, thoughts, and dreams. Voice is your expressed knowledge and wisdom, even your repressed fears. Your soul finds expression in voice, and voice needs communication.

Even with advanced technology and social media, Americans—and citizens around the world—are starved for lack of voice. As censorship continues against those who don't fit within the cardboard narrative, we are facing a growing pent-up need to talk, listen, and dialogue.

Voice includes the questions you ask and the insights you give. In order to be validated, voice needs open discussion. Discussion is the key to liberating voice. It is, however, essential to understand that voice must be connected to a vote: it has to be a function of a group making a decision together. This is what we've never really perfected in human history. We've never really mastered voice in connection with a vote. Voice needs an open forum in which a vote can take place. In fact, the closer we connect *voice* to *vote*, the less uniformed apprehension we have toward each other. Shared consent naturally challenges all votes equally. A vote unchallenged by its peers is subject to the bent mind of an ignorant freedom.

If it is *just* a vote we have, with no equal expression for voice to influence votes, we have a serious problem—we have the America we're living in currently. Without voice connected to a vote, we empower those with the biggest megaphone and the most influence. Over time, we've given our voice to the authority we worship in power. Eventually those in power build smaller boxes—and never hear our voice.

Perhaps this is the hidden meaning in the saying, "think outside the box." As long as thinking doesn't affect the power structure inside the box, go ahead and think outside the box all you want! Uninformed apprehension becomes the norm. New ideas remain limp with no teeth in a vote. We support the hardline discrimination of voice because we assume the vote is where all the power is. This is not true. The real power is getting more voice inside the box where the decisions are made.

Contrary to what many think, it is very easy to control people. All you need is to centralize your voice. Vote has never been the thing those in control want. They want control of voice. If you can control voice by limiting who can speak and what can be heard, you can easily control the vote and the outcome.

Compare what we experience in the United States today with the system under the Cambridge Agreement of 1632. Here's the complete agreement:

An Agreement by a General Conference for a Monthly Meeting

Every person under subscribed shall meet Every second Monday in Every month within the meetinghouse In the Afternoon within half an hour after the ringing of the bell and that every one that make not his personal appearance there and continues there without leave... until meeting bee Ended shall for every default pay twelve pence and if it be not paid next meeting then to double it and so until it is paid.[1]

---

[1]Lutz, Donald S. Colonial Origins of the American Constitution. Liberty Fund, Indianapolis, IN 1998. P 64

The Cambridge Agreement can be seen as a founding document for the United States. If we look at how we organized locally before we had a federal government, what we'll see is that we experienced greater open discussion, wider participation, and transparent communication. While men and women didn't have equal voting rights at first, the means of discussion were superior to what we have today. Can you imagine a policy requiring every citizen to meet and share their voice, or pay a fine? Over the years, we've allowed the loss of voice to take place where "everyone" turns into a "few," and those few have gotten control. We falsely assume there isn't room for everyone to be involved. If we believe this, we have no imagination—and the American experiment in self-government will remain dead. Until liberty has equal voice for all, we will continue down this path of a divided and divisive vote.

Round Tables and Open Forums

There's no solid evidence that King Arthur's "knights of the round table" ever existed. It doesn't matter; we still have the ideal etched into our minds. The model of a round table encourages something powerful; it puts everything into the open with no figurehead in control.

This open round table concept only works when everyone is sitting at the table with equal voice, not working behind the scenes in factions and parties. The only way to stop behind-the-scenes manipulation is to abolish the majority rule that strengthens power centers.

Imagine two nonprofit organizations, each with a board of directors. One board makes decisions by a two-thirds majority vote and the other requires one hundred percent unanimous consent. Which board would you rather sit on? If you say a majority vote, you're a political person—you seek power and you align with power. If you say unanimous consent, you're an advocate for others—you seek freedom and you require equal voice to protect liberty.

The voice of consent exists to move things forward, and the voice of dissent exists to hold things up. They both come from the freedom of individual responsibility. Each person on a board must retain both powers if they hope to remain free in their voice.

The first power is used to stop controlling interests driven by curved intentions (the liberty of dissent). The second power is used to move good decisions forward (the liberty of consent). If consent cannot be reached, at least no power is in control, and everything remains on the table for continued discussion. There's absolutely nothing wrong with this. Unanimous consent in small groups is the only way to protect the liberty of consent and the liberty of dissent. It doesn't define what the best modular structure or decentralized organization to do this might look like, it only recognizes the importance of every person at the table.

If you don't believe that such a practice can work, or that it can be scaled up, look at one of the least-known inspirations for the United States Constitution, the *Five Nation Iroquois Confederacy*. This document protects the two core principles of liberty: our will to consent and our will to dissent. In fact, the *Five Nation Confederacy* is the longest living participatory democracy in world history.

The word Iroquois ("people of the longhouse") refers to a band of five tribes: the Mohawk, Oneida, Onondaga, Cayuga and Seneca nations. A sixth nation, the Tuscarora, joined the confederacy later.

The most striking quality of the Iroquois nation is its ability to reach common consent through a long-format discussion. The lords, men typically selected by a matriarchy, gather in a long-house and the individual councils from each tribe gather separately in the same longhouse. Here is a small section of the Five Nations Confederate Council:

All the business of the Five Nations Confederate Council shall be conducted by the two combined bodies of Confederate Lords. First, the question shall be passed upon by the Mohawk and Seneca Lords, then it shall be discussed and passed by the Oneida and Cayuga Lords. Their decisions shall be referred to the Onondaga Lords, (fire Keepers) for final judgment. The same process shall obtain when a question is brought before the council by an individual or a War Chief.

In all cases the procedure must be as follows: when the Mohawk and Seneca Lords have unanimously agreed upon a question, they shall report their decision to the Cayuga and Oneida Lords who shall deliberate upon the question and report a unanimous decision to the Mohawk Lords. The Mohawk Lords will then report the standing of the case to the Fire Keepers, who shall render a decision as they see fit in case of a disagreement by the two bodies, or confirm the decisions of the two bodies if they are identical. The Fire Keepers shall then report their decision to the Mohawk Lords who shall announce it to the open council.

If though any misunderstanding of obstinacy on the part of the Fire Keepers, they render a decision at variance with that of the Two Sides, the Two Sides shall reconsider the matter and if their decisions are jointly the same as before they shall report to the Fire Keepers who are then compelled to confirm their joint decision.[2]

Even when moving a subject along through each council and through all tribes in the long house, the demand for greater consent maintains the social responsibility within the hands of the people. There's no popular majority vote at any level, because it would nullify discussion and circumvent dissent. If such a culture can master this process for several hundred years, all we have to do is scale it in the context of micro-local republics. If there's one thing we're good at doing, it's scaling just about anything from the smallest ignition point!

Throughout history we have many examples of the impact that wide consent can have. Both the *Charter of Liberties* (1100) and the *Magna Carta* (1215) were created from the experience of a widened participation of involved consent. Then, in 1776, we had the Declaration of Independence. The vote was almost unanimous with only New York abstaining. At that point, the *Declaration* was the greatest document of consent from the greatest number of involved participants in world history. It did not unite five tribes; it united thirteen colonies.

Then the French created the *Tennis Court Oath* in 1789, passed by 576 of the 577 members in the Third Estate. The *United States Constitution*, in 1788, was passed by 39 of 55 delegates, and later three of the nine state legislatures, Delaware, New Jersey and Georgia, quickly ratified the Constitution by unanimous consent.

---

[2]Constitution of the Iroquois Nations: The Great Binding Law, Gayanashagowa. www.constituion.org/cons/iroquois-p.html

The remaining state legislatures voted approximately 977 to 577 in favor of the Constitution.

The point is, we have many historical examples indicating that wide consent is possible. In fact, typically, the greater the consent we require of ourselves, the greater the liberty we create. We have lost the importance of wide consent because we have taken the low road of central control.

Never forget this: Freedom is not forced disconnection, which is the culture we have become in America. Freedom is *voluntary* connection, it's the people we can become. We need voluntary connection to freedom, and this is what those who advocate the Low Road are frightened that people will figure out. Once we get our voice back, we will want control of our value. When this happens, we are facing a second American founding that we can only hope will become a fresh start.

Grovelers, Snivelers, and Panderers

Have you ever wondered how those with no genuine voice or real value get into positions of power? Have you noticed that, more and more across our country—even throughout the world—fewer people are able to stand up for their own visions and ideas?

Why do we allow oligarchs in the media, technocrats in technology, and bureaucrats in government get so much control and centralize so much power in such tiny boxes? It's because we have allowed them to build an army of grovelers, snivelers, and panderers. The more we centralize power, the more we attract the worst to that power.

Grovelers are the most docile; we see a lot of them because of how we organize into top-down and centrally controlled power. A groveler is a person who crawls, face down and body prostrated, in abject humility and fear. Grovelers are not bipedal—they don't stand upright. This is all metaphoric, but you get the point.

Grovelers are talented at kowtowing to authority. The term *kowtow* is derived from "koutou" in Mandarin. It is the act of prostration—that is, of kneeling and bowing so low that one's head is touching the ground. In East Asian culture, the kowtow is the highest sign of reverence. While expressed as a physical and outward gesture in the East, it is subversive and hidden in the West.

The highest form of kowtow in the West is groveling. Groveling isn't physical prostration, it's mental subjugation. It is anti-American.

When you give grovelers power, they will obey. They will never let you down, but they will also never lift you up. They are a protective shield against snivelers.

Snivelers don't kowtow. They are complainers. They nag and whine about how they never advance in power. They complain about every itch they have. In fact, they derive their only power by pointing out problems to those in power. If you have an organization with a lot of snivelers, just put one in power and that one person will begin groveling to you. All you need to do to shut up a sniveler, and gain their allegiance, is to give them power. From then on, a sniveler will start to hire grovelers. Hiring a sniveler who becomes a groveler is often done to shield those in authority from snivelers. Snivelers can't stand other snivelers! It takes one to know one.

Snivelers aren't anti-American: they are simply not Americans. Snivelers speak up because they are not in power, so all they can do is dig holes of doubt they can never fill with a better idea.

Lastly, we have panderers. A panderer is someone who tries to please others for an ulterior motive or a curved intention. A panderer kisses up in order to get something. Like a dishonest salesperson, panderers tell you what you want to hear. Politicians are often panderers, as they'll say or do anything to get a vote, keep power, or raise money. A panderer is one who caters to or exploits the lowest tastes or desires of others. It's locker-room talk. It's a "when in Rome" attitude: do exactly as they do. It's promising free stuff from the public treasury in exchange for getting voted into power. Sometimes we need to pander to the enemy to give a false confidence in times of war, but life is not always about war.

If you want someone who will protect your power, hire a panderer; that's how people in controlling power think. They think in terms of those who will follow, those who will obey, and those who will not step out of line. Panderers will do as they're told *if* you pander to their desires for a little power of their own. They will make you look good—but only if you redirect some of that light back to them. Panderers tend to be self-absorbed and narcissistic. They are plastic. You can melt them to make them into what you want. Under heat, they easily give up pliability for stiff compliance. With obedience that cannot think for itself, you will be required to do all the thinking and all the value creation yourself.

Be warned, though: panderers will hire grovelers and snivelers to bolster their power. And panderers are known for switching allegiance. They are used as a temporary means to justify certain ends. If you dare use them, use them for a short spell. Too long and they will get control.

Panderers are intelligent enough to know who has the real power, and so they deliver what those in power want. Panderers aren't as self-debasing as grovelers, nor are they as insecure as snivelers. They are political puppets. They give what those in power want. They are driven strictly by self-preservation. They are not true Americans, but America is overwhelmed by them. Power loves to hire them as a means to protect what those in power have.

Here are three things to remember: the more we centralize power, the more a multitude of informers, moles, and turncoats will get control. Around the world, and in America, they have gotten control of many mid-level positions throughout society because we fell for the oldest trick in the book, the worship of authority, which attracts the worst from the population. Every time we centralize power, here's what we attract.

- Grovelers, the most docile.
- Snivelers, the most demanding.
- Panderers, the most dangerous.

All three shut down voice, and voice is where true power lies, because voice influences vote. Grovelers, snivelers, and panderers appease and pacify those in power by shutting down and censoring voice that seeks to challenge that power. If you want to know more about the character traits of those who destroy entire organizations and nations, read *The Political Optimist*, the book before *The High Road*. It details the character traits of truly destructive personalities.

Let's ask a basic question. What is a vote with no teeth? It's like eating steak without a tongue. This is how important voice is to a vote, and why any new fresh start will fail if it doesn't keep vote and voice equally connected. Grovelers, snivelers, and panderers understand the power that voice has to a vote, which is why they spend their time keeping out-the-box voice separated from in-the-box vote. It's how they appease those in power and how they maintain their position as gatekeepers to the king.

Vote and Voice

As we are beginning to see, voice is the great power, and when not separated from a vote, it remains in the hands of the people. When it's separated, we have tyranny. The greater the separation, the greater the darkness. A vote can validate our freedom, provided we have an equal voice in deciding what to vote on. Increasing our voice will be the greatest challenge of the future, especially since the compliant class and the established power structure will fight it. Voice and vote work best together and never apart.

Our vote is our free agency. It is our will. Vote represents our decisions, a personal agreement with others; it is a citizenship signature. Voting is a choice given voluntarily and without coercion—provided, of course, there is equal voice. Vote is democratic consent, and it works best in discussion, where every voice is allowed to be challenged before a vote is cast and where all votes must come to consensus. Voice is the only means to reach consensus, and consensus is the absence of uniformed apprehension.

Never forget: vote has its greatest impact when it's in the same room where all voice is being expressed. If people are intimidated—or pressured—to vote a certain way (as is the case when there's a simple majority decision of 51%), a vote is under pressure. Or worse, it is bullied—or shamed into submission.

It's time we admit that the founders of the American Constitution failed to build an equality of voice in connection with an equality of vote. The second American founding will do this—and compromised people in power will fight against it along with their legions of grovelers, snivelers, and panderers. Aristocracies still exist (as they have always existed); they hire the weak to maintain control. The grovelers, snivelers, and panderers are the enemy that will fight greater democratic consent.

Today we see an increasing amount of uniformed apprehension turning to the false liberty of self-protectionism. This happens by shutting out voice. Like the man at the fence who turned his back on Atlas and walked to his house, we aren't required to listen to any ideas that exist beyond our fence. The problem with America is that we have no requirement to participate and become more informed through open and vigorous discussion.

County commissioners lack a wide reach of voice in the community. City councils barely tolerate hearing local citizens. School boards are too small and easily intimidated by state boards of education. Corporations bend to their presidents, and the presidents of universities pander to the state board of regents, who are then subject to interlocking corporate directorships, which quietly and secretly influence college accrediting agencies. If not accredited, you cannot receive federal dollars; universities can therefore be controlled. Spend a decade or two working in higher education, and in time the power structure reveals itself. The average American university is not a place for ideas: curved intentions and the cardboard of linear thinking dominate instead.

Hierarchies, even religious organizations, are maintained by political gamesmanship and power struggles. When the leader of a world religion refuses to stand against the child abuse committed by hundreds of leaders within the church, and when he hushes it up, we know he is a panderer himself, an aristocrat compromised by a hidden monarchy. The real disease is our increasing loss of voice, managed by centralized powers.

We're now witnessing what happens when we destroy voice and install vote alone. It produces a kind of freedom inside an iron grid where everyone is isolated in personal self-interest. It's a frenzy of disconnect that centralizes voice into the hands of a few—and those few put a compliant class in power they can easily control.

Censorship of voice is the signature move of compliant and compromised people. As long as we keep putting individuals in power with no access to challenge their vote freely, those daring to share an idea or propose a new innovation will be shut out. A renaissance in voice will save America. Anything else is a half measure.

From now on, any new idea in human organization must decentralize the control of voice and make it equal to a vote. The future of American Greatness is dependent on the marriage of vote and voice. Whether it's a democracy or a republic, things work better when people have more voice—not less. Having an equal voice in perfect agreement with a vote is the exact action that defines the very best of a democratic republic.

While a republic protects voice by division and separation of powers, a democracy maintains the workings of voice. Together they have the potential to become more powerful for good. In a democracy, it's easier to divide voice from a vote, and in a republic, we just divide the vote to create separation of powers. A fresh start must dare to create a *better* democratic process that protects the importance of voice to keep the power in the hands of the people. When we learn to combine the two, we will have a more perfect union. In the future, common sense will look for this to happen. It will look for a renaissance in voice.

If it's tabulated honestly, we have a vote, but what makes our freedom most valid is having our voice equally measured with our vote. Accomplish this, and we include value at the same time.

Value

Value is the third unique quality that validates human liberty. Everyone doesn't have the same value to offer at any given moment. Some add greater value than others. Some are handicapped and cannot add much value, some hoard value, and, yes, some are lazy and take value.

What is value?

Value is our wealth, our time, and our energy. Value is something added. Value is regenerative; it sustains individuals, communities, and cultures. At its purest, value is creation. Ideally, it's what we give without force, and it's what we make without theft. Value is the field we plant, and the service we give.

In today's democracies, value is not conserved in the hands that create it. It is stolen, taxed, and burdened with debt. The only way value is protected is if it has voice and vote to conserve it in the hands of the people and communities that created it. This isn't selfishness. It's a fresh start at freedom. But if we burden value creation with control from faraway hands, communities die.

We could say value is the most precious of the three validations of human freedom, because it gives the satisfaction of accomplishing something; voice and vote don't offer this kind of fulfillment. Value alone manifests voice and vote in a concrete and objective form. Value is how we exhibit our ideas and showcase our freedom.

If we express our freedom by adding value but we don't have the voice to protect and conserve that value, we lose motivation in creation. We then fall to the fear of uninformed apprehension, our communities turn to scarcity, selfishness, self-protectionism, and, finally, uninformed apprehension. America has been sliding faster and faster into this pit for decades, and we're approaching a day when all value is created and controlled without our voice. We've heard the phrase, "you will own nothing, and you will be happy." These are the words of a controlling mind on the low road. If we own nothing of value, we have no voice in the creation or protection of that value. We call this serfdom and slavery.

There is nothing that brings people together better than having value in common, protected in the hands that create it, further incentivizing the creation of more value. A new American Greatness will create more voice as a core principle to inspire the adding of more value. We cannot inspire more value creation in entrepreneurism—or in community service—without a greater culture of consent that supports more voice.

If you were the devil, and if you had only one freedom to take from people in order to control them, which freedom would you take? Their vote, their voice, or their value? You'd want their value for sure; but you couldn't take it directly. You'd have to settle for their voice. The answer is voice.

If you wanted to control value creation, you'd first have to shut down, censor, and limit voice. It's difficult for others to complain when their value is taken from them! When you get people backed into corners with no voice, you can usurp all their value and place their creation under centralized control. We don't need twisted and convoluted conspiracies of treachery to prove this. We can see it happen in health care, education, welfare services, public land use, energy, and more. Value is controlled every day without your voice. If you want to find out why so much uninformed apprehension is getting worse, it's because we are being separated from caring about what we can create together. We comply and compromise to stay alive.

If you want to kill a culture, this is how you do it. Limit voice into a centralized authority, and place all control of value creation in the hands of that central authority, which then hires grovelers, snivelers, and panderers to maintain that control. Uninformed apprehension—which is basically self-isolation—happens when people realize there is nothing to protect the value they have to add to the community, so they choose to retreat and hide.

A fresh start can only begin with the creation of an equal voice. With equal voice comes the conservation of value in the hands of individuals, communities, and cultures that created it. This will then incentivize the volunteer creation of more value. The future of American Greatness is dependent on our ability to unite the three as one. There is only one leader who can do this, and it is not the leader many think.

What is Leadership?

For decades, Americans have read one leadership book after another. We now suffer from too much focus on the qualities and traits of leadership without qualifying how great leadership works. Before we can organize a fresh start in American Greatness, it is wise to know the difference in leaders. There are three kinds of leaders:

1. Those who take control.
2. Those who take charge.
3. Those who take responsibility.

Take-control leaders attract people willing to compromise their freedom for a position in the hierarchy. Take-control leaders build organizations of followers rather than independent and free minds. They centralize voice in order to control all value. They breed protectionism and build vertically integrated power structures filled with grovelers, snivelers, and panderers. Only the most compliant personality can function under a take-control leader.

Take-control leaders have little empathy for humanity. They stifle innovation and lose good people—fast. Nothing is sustainable or lasting, unless they collude with other take-control leaders to shut out competition. This happens more often than we realize. For obvious reasons, take-control leaders have a very low threshold of acceptance for new ideas and dissident outliers. They want followers and flatterers, not self-reliant minds.

Next are *take-charge leaders.* Take-charge leaders are the first to jump in. They get things done ... but always alone. They are workers and they outperform everyone in productivity. They don't have a patient nature that mentors others to take charge. If others do follow, take-charge leaders are comfortable telling everyone what to do, but never how or why. They never explain the workings. Things do get done with take-charge leaders, but they make everyone dependent on them for direction and productivity. The worst thing about take-charge leaders is that everything falls apart when they leave because the entire system was dependent on them. True Americans don't like to be dependent on one person. If your organization is in a mess, go ahead and hire a take-charge leader, but be warned: you will be completely dependent on them for the duration of their stay and beyond.

Last are *take-responsibility leaders.* This is the most undervalued and misunderstood leader. A leader that takes responsibility is the leader we have lost in America—and we need them! This leader's true nature, what they do naturally, is to take responsibility.

Taking responsibility is about setting up systems and processes that others can follow so they can, in turn, take charge and take responsibility in perfecting those systems and processes.

At their core, take-responsibility leaders protect the voice of every person, focusing on securing liberty for others. By returning to the *Constitution* and the *Bill of Rights*, the focus of leadership can be to protect liberty. However, for a new America destined to become greater, voice will be at the heart of what this leader will protect. In fact, the leaders that take responsibility by creating systems that perfect voice in connection with a vote will be the founders of a new American Greatness. It is no doubt that this leader will achieve the promise of heaven on earth.

Systems that liberate more voice in connection with a vote will be some of the most liberating ever created in history. They will give not only voice to more Americans, but involve consent to conserve value in the hands that create that value. Again, this is not selfishness as the Low Road would lead you to believe. It is sustainable and the purest form of conservation possible.

If our politicians could think like this, we could fulfill America's destiny to be that light on a hill for the rest of the world once again. That day is coming.

No More Polar Opposites
In the United States, two existing ideas find themselves in direct opposition to each other—simply because it's what the underworld's controlling entities want.

The first idea is "Count my Vote."
The second idea is "Keep my Voice."

Let's explain what each means individually to reveal a serious problem. The Count My Vote crowd says we need to remove physical barriers so every person can vote. If citizens are forced to attend a meeting to discuss policies and principles to adopt as well as political candidates, it's a barrier to those who cannot physically attend.

This point of view says that if a person needs to show identification and they are required to vote in person; both are considered barriers to voting. Therefore, these barriers are discriminatory, and we should give everyone an easy vote. Voting in person should be done away with and made entirely online—or through mail-in voting—to make it easier for all to vote.

Greater voter participation does not mean more informed voting. It just means more voters are involved.

The argument for Count My Vote is slanted away from the equality of voice. Those who advocate counting votes only do so by calling any work required to cast a vote outside the cubicle of one's home racist, prejudicial, and non-democratic. Hidden in their motive is the truth: they want to control the voice in order to control the vote.

The focus for Count My Vote is a vote only. Just about everything we see happening today is being done to make a vote self-isolated and uninformed, and all in the name of accessibility. "Vote by mail" is the greatest hoax used by the Low Road to push us further apart. The true intention is to give power to just a few with voice to both influence and count the vote. In the name of fairness and efficiency, we are shutting down voice to almost nothing. Next will come voting through the Internet, again all pushed in the name of getting more voter involvement while controlling the voice that determines the outcome of the vote.

Count My Vote should be "give my consent." But it is not. Having a vote counted is not really giving your consent. It is like taking a number and waiting in line at the deli. Meanwhile the people ahead of you in line are influencing the kitchen about what specials will be on the menu for the day. A vote alone has no influence if you are not at the head of the line. You can have your vote counted, but to give real consent is to have your voice heard before anyone casts a vote.

They say, "every vote counts." This is true in the mathematical sense. Every vote, we hope, should count. But a vote does not necessarily count toward creating policy, making decisions, promoting ideas, or asking questions. A vote will never challenge another vote, not until we launch a fresh start that unites vote with voice.

Those who place emphasis on the vote know they can manipulate many Americans suffering from uninformed apprehension. If not that, they can maintain control of those who hold to the same curved intentions. Controlling power pushes for popular voting outside public meetings and outside local discussion. The proven way to maintain control is to move decisions under central control where voice is easily managed and manipulated. America suffers under the growing suppression of voice, and we need to stop it with a fresh start.

Keep My Voice, on the other hand, has deep connections to the free expression of an idea. It is all about making sure voice is heard. Having a vote does not include your thoughts about what should be voted on. Rarely included are all the possible choices available to vote on. This is where voice matters; it has the power to influence what we should vote on.

"Keep My Voice" should be "Keep My Voice with My Vote." The only way this can happen is to give voice equal footing with a vote. This requires conversation, meetings, discussion, and open involvement with others in the same room where we vote. Future leaders that take responsibility will create systems and processes that will include more voice with a vote, and they will make them inseparable.

The founding fathers understood this to some degree when they required all senators to be elected by state legislatures, where there is both voice and vote in the same room. We then changed this with the Seventeenth Amendment, which required all senators to be elected by popular majority vote by the people. When this happened, we suddenly gave more power to the media, big money, and various power centers that have more command over voice to influence the vote.

We now know what to look for in a coming renaissance. We now know the High Road is a more informed democracy that eliminates uniformed apprehension. In order for everyone to effectively take part, it must keep both voice and vote together in order to inspire more added value.

Let the American experiment in self-government begin again with a fresh start. Common sense now has some teeth. Anytime we see voice and vote separated, we know something is wrong. Anytime we can join them together, we know something is right.

Hope for America

In our ignorance or fear we assume existing power is all there is, or that the controlling leviathan we call the state cannot be moved. We are afraid to rock the boat. We fear being punished by authority or ostracized by the dirty tricks of a new sophisticated rejection culture. Many Americans now falsely believe that people cannot work together.

We cannot wait for a champion or trusted leader to come fix things, because we have seen that person become corrupted. Most Americans have all but lost trust in each other and in leadership as the solution. We have surrendered the American experiment in self-government to intimidation. Like a noxious weed, the growth of uninformed apprehension has consumed the nation. We elect paid representatives to pull weeds, but many in power justify planting more weeds instead. A growing apathy leads to more division and greater disconnection.

Our disunited population is not broken because of racism peddled by those with opaque intentions. We are divided because we've fallen to the idolatrous worship of centralized authority. We are told by high-minded snobs that we are too small-minded to manage life on our own in our communities. We feel crushed and lack the vision for a fresh start that could build trust in people again. America needs reuniting, not under a nationalist movement, but as a single gust of wind that nobody can refute.

That gust of wind is the fusing of a trinity no controlling authority can deny without revealing its true motive: control.

We need to believe people can work together to accomplish great things. In other words, we don't need to give authority over to a single person or a central hierarchy. We need to take responsibility. Taking responsibility is our greatest power as a people, and our greatest right as individuals. Taking responsibility best exhibits what it means to move the cause of liberty. If we speak up and say we're going to take power back, this threatens those in power and usually leads to revolution.

Instead of protests, pickets, or polls, what if we the people decided to simply take responsibility? What if we could wise up to the mechanics of control and simply avoid using those mechanics?

If we could easily see the operations of a bad control system and how it works to maintain control, and if we could see a better system to operate, then we could see a better world. Even without a better way to organize, more open debate would suffice.

Here's a framework to start us thinking:

Suppose communities across the United States decided to meet up and agree on one idea. Suppose that one idea is to protect each person's voice with their vote. Here's what would happen. We would first start to meet in smaller groups. Once these groups began to talk and build trust—while protecting each person's voice and vote—they could form any necessary alliances with other groups. As they grew, no coercion could be placed on the youngest or even most literate participant. This provision for a simple core guide could be the bane of existing hierarchies. Those in power would fight against it, just like so many controlling powers in European history tried to shut down the voice of opposing religious views.

When different views are allowed, more of us can see those views. But to those on the Low Road, if any view of God or the state is seen in the wrong way, a curved intention takes hold, and so the people must be controlled. In many countries in Europe it was illegal to meet in public without a proper religious authority's permission. Freedom was forced to stand up.

We are facing that same fate, not by a religious authority, but by something we'll reveal shortly when we discuss the Low Road.

As long as those in power are allowed to keep moving the action of liberty at bay, intimidation will grow and feed a compliant class inside the power structure. No majority can be swayed by false promises, no special counsel can be given power to complicate the obvious, and no hunger for control will be fed.

No lawyer would be needed, and the vote of an academic would not be any more valid than that of a recent high-school graduate.

A word of warning: CEOs, deans, HOA presidents, principals, and bureau chiefs—including all the zealots that worship their authority—will not like this one bit. They will try to complicate or control it, or they will demand the creation of a committee they can shame and intimidate. Those in control will not want to find solutions and invite new vision into the open commons. They will never let those who are involved put out a new idea. They will thwart the wide-spectrum study and the culture of consent.

Take note now of those who hate this exercise and those who fight against it. Identify those who want an amendment of the one core principle that gives voice and vote equal footing for all. Learn to recognize how they will separate voice from vote to give themselves an edge. These are the ones most addicted to power. They are trained to take control, not how to take responsibility.

We cannot fix those who already have this illness, this need to control, but we can fix the systems that breed the illness. We do not need to infect other organizations with the same mechanics that spread the virus. We can stop feeding the virus entirely and let it starve itself into a natural death.

Top-down control structures have been the norm throughout human history, as anyone who has looked closely at the world's governmental structures would agree. Whether these corrosive types of governance infect small warring clans or massive hierarchies with armies, it doesn't matter. Central control doesn't work. Centralized control structures have brought out the worst in humanity and not the best. And the communities that fail to take common sense measures to resolve conflict, will lose their liberty once again. The American experiment in self-government (that started primarily in the 18th century) will have failed. We must imagine a fresh start now, before it's too late.

Certainly addressing our human nature openly and uniformly would help communities maintain their liberty by creating structures that aren't easily manipulated. We could avoid the practice of woke shaming altogether, and instead teach children about the lures of control that aren't naturally American. And just as our first founders separated themselves from a controlling nightmare, we, too, can use common sense of voice and vote in tandem to separate ourselves from our own controlling nightmare.

If we don't speak up in protest, and instead just take responsibility quietly into our hands, then there will be no need for a revolution. We don't need to ask for permission, we just need to take responsibility. Think of it as taking a deep breath: the fresh air is there for everyone to take.

Imagine all the areas where responsibility is open for the taking: health care, education, welfare services, agriculture, housing, and a host of other social responsibilities. The list is long. Some are easy to take, others will require greater consent from more people. We are wrong to assume we cannot organize to take responsibility for any—or all—of these. Moving the cause of liberty is not about moving the pendulum from Big Brother to individual rights; it's about moving the pendulum from cancel culture to community culture. We are in a cold civil war against intimidating power unlike anything we've ever seen. This power is hell-bent on controlling every nook and cranny of society "for our own good."

Oligarchs in government, business, religion, and education want to maintain control by funding educational programs to give them a foothold in marketing the bad logic of cardboard brown to unsuspecting believers. Some even fund riots in the streets to maintain the divisiveness in the people, which keeps them in power. The new *die* culture promoted by the dons of arrogance in our universities lie to American youth by erasing common sense. Their *diversity* is actually death to free speech. Their *inclusion* is more isolation. And their *equity* is the perpetuation of inequality. The "Saad Truth"[3] is that this is not a lie, it is just a sophisticated way to die. The cancel culture is not a rising tide that lifts all ships, it is the inrushing sea before a tsunami. Cancel culture doesn't build culture, it kills community.

Tortured and abused words have become banners of war to an army of social-justice zombies. Each "woke" soldier signals personal virtue by waving twisted terms with borrowed and hollow meaning. Terms like "micro-aggression" are used aggressively to silence debate. "Critical race theory" promotes a whole new racism. And phrases like "gender-binary," "white privilege," and "toxic masculinity" act like anvils, sledgehammers, and pickaxes competing for no purpose other than to express deep-seated anger.

Filled with extreme hatred, promoters of cancel culture are never happy. They destroy democratic context in favor of the cardboard brown of linear thinking. As in Orwell's Ministry of Love, the catechism of cancel culture gnaws at our faces like rats until we snitch on each other and kowtow to the pressure of its bent bias.

Our voice is our only connection to peaceful assembly, not the submission of our conscience to the campus-diversity czar.

---

[3]Dr. Saad, https://thesaadtruthwithdrsaad.podbean.com

Voice is how we know we have liberty. Any attempt to silence, censor, or shut down voice is not only a threat to liberty, it's a threat to peace. Voice is the first quality in a trinity that defines each person's liberty. And today voice is under attack by an anti-humanitarian totalitarianism that makes hard-line religious totalitarianism look timid.

America is sick from the wrong kind of leadership, and we need hope in a common sense that everyone can breathe deeply once again. We follow the cult of personality with no voice. This is intolerable. We think giving equal voice is impossible, unrealistic, and logistically not feasible. We think someone needs to be in charge.

None of this is true, especially for the majority of our communities' and states' decisions. We have lost our imagination for self-government.

Once we see how powerful voice is when conjoined with a vote, we will begin to see new organizational structures that properly unite the two to protect our valued creations from unwanted theft and control.

A Third Eye

After having struggled with his father's trinity (subject, predicate, and object) needed to define the epistemology of meaning needed to challenge physics and philosophy, Atlas finally found the trinity of voice, vote, and value. As long as all three are preserved inside each individual, and inside each neighborhood, community, county, and state, we will find the path to an American Greatness that will once again be the envy of the world. Atlas found his third eye, his own voice for the predicate reality his father had realized in studying physics.

Sometimes it takes a few generations in one family and many iterations of one philosophy to finally simplify what has been complex for too long. We call this *long-format discussion* and *wide-body consensus*. Leaders who take responsibility will treasure both, no matter how long it takes, and no matter how hard it will be to get many to adopt.

For now, with the trinity that validates our freedom (voice, vote, and value), we face a fork in the path to the High Road. The fork leads down to the Low Road or up the High Road. It is not really a fork at all. It is more like a decision. The decision is now before us; we can either choose greater informed consent or die under the suffocation of uniformed apprehension.

We're told two heads are better than one. We are about to see what those two heads believe, and why they are so powerful when they work together rather than apart.

CHAPTER 3 The High Road

And the Lord smelled a sweet savor; and the Lord said in his heart,
I will not again curse the ground any more for man's sake; for the
imagination of man's heart is evil from his youth; neither will I again
smite any more everything living, as I have done.

—GENESIS 8:21

Birth of Belief

In the delivery room at the County Hospital in Sanpete County, Utah, a baby in distress was stuck in his mother's pelvis. He would not budge. Despite the epidural, Ann, the mother, wanted to collapse.

Worried about the stress on the baby, the doctor reached for tools wrapped in plastic. He first applied a suction cup against the baby's head, where it slid around until it centered itself on the baby's crown. When he made his first pull, the doctor fell back a bit, nearly off his stool. You could hear the baby's heartbeat increase on the monitor as the suction cup popped off. The doctor stopped and grabbed forceps; a sight as painful to see as the epidural injection in Ann's back.

The doctor inserted the steel spoons around the baby's crowning head. In Atlas's mind, the image was like tongs trying to grab

93

a rotten head of cabbage stuck in the sink disposal. Ann couldn't feel the cold metal, but she could feel its wrench. Clamping the head between the cold forceps, the doctor pulled. The clamps slipped off and the doctor fell back again. He tried once more, bracing his knee against the table, telling Ann to push.

As he pulled hard and Ann pushed, the doctor again went backward, this time falling off the stool with the baby in tow. The umbilical cord looped to the ground like a thick electrical line, and almost as heavy. Ann endured a third-degree tear even despite the two episiotomies.

The doctor quickly got up and pinched the umbilical cord with a clamp to stop the bleeding. It took both hands using surgical scissors for Atlas to cut the cord, which was surprisingly difficult.

A nurse received the baby and immediately emptied its lungs of fluid. A baby under stress often discharges feces in the uterus. If this happens, the baby's lungs become infected, and illness follows, so the nurse took a long tube and slipped it down the infant's throat. A small diaphragm in the nurse's hands drew up the liquid and she rubbed the baby's spine with a stiff knuckle. A loud, gurgling cry filled the room.

Atlas looked down at the child and said quietly, "Another fish out of water." He then touched the bruised smudge on his son's forehead.

"We call that a stork mark," the doctor replied.

"It looks like a smudge."

"It goes away in time," the nurse said.

The nurse was correct, the bruise did go away. However, the trauma of birth did not.

The nurse picked up the baby and handed him to Ann. In her own quiet whisper, while receiving the infant boy in her arms, she said, "You are born good."

In the same moment Atlas was thinking the baby was "born free."

That birth took place over twenty-five years ago. Many times in life we are faced with a question. How do we decide what to believe? What does it mean to be good? What does it mean to be free? Even if the "imagination of man's heart is evil from his youth,"[1] can we choose to believe and act differently from that teaching?

Certain moments in life produce burning questions. We don't realize the impact of the question until years later when we're finally able to find an answer from countless hours of self-discovery. For Atlas, the answer remained divisive until it germinated the hope for a fresh start.

The Question

Many people say that what constitutes American Greatness is rugged individualism. This assumes American Greatness can only be achieved by a single individual. A lot of Americans get angry when they hear that, because they don't believe in individualism. They believe in collectivism—we are not great alone; we are great when we give our allegiance to something bigger than ourselves. Unfortunately, that "something bigger" is usually an all-powerful sovereign—like the government. The idea of state collectivism makes those who believe in individualism equally mad as hell.

The challenge with both rugged individualism and state collectivism is that neither explains how to create American Greatness. One side argues that American culture is great just as it is. The other side believes American culture is rotten and must die to make way for a new progressive agenda. One view carries the con-

---

[1]Genesis 8:21, King James Version.

notation that rugged individualism is "selfish determination." The other view speaks of "a new world order" that promises to "build back better" under complete central control. Neither makes for a great sell. Both have curved intentions that ignore the common sense that explains how American Greatness works.

So, how exactly does American Greatness work? If rugged individualism leans toward isolation, and if global collectivism is the death of neighborliness in exchange for a zealous dependence on authority, what can bring people to the table? How do we help individualists know that they are needed in the community? How do we help collectivists see that while taking care of the poor and respecting different cultures and their regional characteristics is a good thing, delegating that important responsibility to outside authorities is not? Where is the third way that brings people together? The way becomes clearer as we recap our journey thus far to the High Road.

Let's Recap
In the first chapter we explained the workings of common sense. The epistemology of meaning is a remedy to the problem of Divided Minds. It's a disciplined process that gives power to take responsibility rather than echo more inactive mental positions with curved intentions.

Asking what love *is*, for example, is not as effective as asking how love *works*. Words like affection, adoration, and infatuation might answer what love is, but they cannot clarify the *meaning* of love. Love, for example, is not a feeling that is shared. It's the action between people. If there is a shared feeling, the action validates it, and not the other way around.

Liberty is similar. Words like freedom, unencumbered, or equality can answer what liberty is, to a degree, but describing how liberty works gets us the real meaning. For example, if we define liberty as the hand that adds value, it is neither objective nor subjective. It is a predicative statement; it shows action and action shows the meaning of a word by answering how it works. The meaning behind the most important words is found in the action. Simply giving a name to an abstract noun, or explaining what a difficult noun is, puts meaning in the hands of curved intentions—which are typically authoritative by nature—and not in the hands of common sense, which shows how it works for all to see.

It's hard to admit that our entire culture in America went wrong when it allowed love to mean anything to anyone … but nothing to everyone. We forgot that we observe the *action* of love best. The action of love describes its meaning much better than we can interpret from feelings that are variable from person to person. In other words, we can say we have the right intention in our hearts, but if the action does not equally reflect that pure intention, we cannot confirm the love.

Until we give common sense a rebirth by demanding recognizable action as the best source of meaning, we will suffer the incremental decline of cultural relativism and the sophistic decay of intellectual obfuscation. We've forgotten that common sense places meaning in the responsible action and not under an assumed authority with curved intentions.

Actions speak louder than words, and we know why.

For decades Americans have begun listening to authority without being aware of their curved intentions. We cannot give up the spirit of common sense.

It's pretty clear. When we ask what something is, we default to authority. When we ask how something works, we default to our own ability to figure it out.

Demanding to know how things work gets us back to the unifying potential of common sense. Asking what something is kneels to an authority to give us the answers.

In the next section, on the Trinity, we considered everything Atlas' father and grandmother had to offer. Atlas then found his own words and the result was a trinity of Voice, Vote, and Value.

Voice is the act of social discourse, discussion, and debate; and voice alone clarifies the best meaning before people decide what to vote on together.

After voice came vote. Vote is our consent when we make decisions as a people. Vote is our free agency to say yes or no.

And, finally, we defined value as the creation we add to the world—our blood, sweat, and tears—the physical and measurable good we put into the world. When voice, vote, and value remain within each individual and in the community, we create more unity. The more we keep each person's voice, vote, and value inseparable from each other, the more we keep authoritarianism from dividing us.

Authoritarians hate this unifying trinity. When free people protect each person's voice, vote, and value, and when they defend all three as sacred and inseparable, authority loses its power to the lifting spirit of common sense. Tyrants shrivel in the light of a popular transparency.

When the founders created the United States, they did not see voice inseparable from a vote. While they were well-read in liberty principles, the founders were novices in building free societies. An early effort to install a shared national reverence for voice and vote inseparable to each other could have prevented much damage to our liberty, but this precaution was missing. The future of American Greatness will depend, in part, on our ability to unite voice with vote as locally as possible. The conservation of value will follow naturally.

Up until now, we haven't known what beliefs are needed to bring people together. This common-sense trinity helps, but people act on belief more than on concepts. That's why those who take the High Road must actually believe in something—something strong enough to motivate the consideration of a better, less traveled, path for the mind. It would help to know all the beliefs that define both the high road and the low road.

The Citizen's Atlas

In his 1964 speech "A Time for Choosing," given when he was campaigning for Barry Goldwater, Ronald Reagan said:

> You and I are told we must choose between a left or right, but I suggest there is no such thing as a left or right. There is only an up or down. Up to man's age-old dream—the maximum of individual freedom consistent with order—or down to the ant heap of totalitarianism.

In the "Citizen's Atlas" below, which came out of a spirit of self-discovery over many years, six beliefs are revealed. Only two have a chance at creating a fresh start with maximum freedom for everyone. These two beliefs will change the world—if they can come together.

The Citizen's Atlas helps eliminate the endless political divide in America by clarifying the meaning of commonly held left and right mindsets. It shows how both left and right perspectives can collapse into dark regions of control. The High Road shows how everything is not a right-wing conspiracy. Instead, the

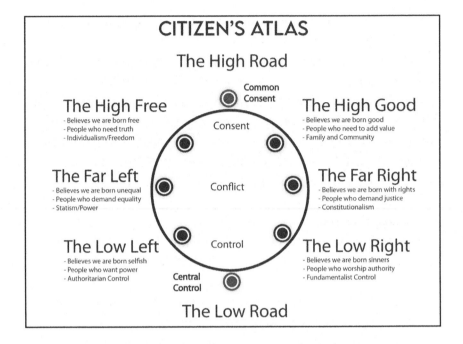

the basket of deplorables are found on the Low Road, which is fed from both sides.

Just as the right has its own pits and potholes, the left has its lies and limitations. Both have a dark underbelly, and common sense demands that we reveal them both.

Using the Citizen's Atlas, we can see that the future of American Greatness depends on replacing central control on the Low Road with the greater transparency of common consent on the High Road.

It can be hard for a mind raised under central control to even fathom giving people greater voice in consent. Those in control will argue against increasing access to the process, at any level and in any organization. They will say it isn't efficient. They will argue that central authority is needed to force compliance with ideas we're told are popular. As long as more than half of us want one thing, the rest had better fall in line.

This is a recipe for lasting turbulence that only a tyrant would attempt to maintain.

Unfortunately, turbulence is like a paid agitator: it's a tool to centralize control and give more power to the tyrant. Like a burned-out middle manager who forgot long ago how to do the actual job, the constant threat of crisis is used to secure more control. We become numb to the turbulence in society and willingly throw up our hands and submit. Those in control will say voice and vote interconnected will never work. They will complicate the process, appeal to authority, and may even cause mayhem in the streets to justify their addiction to more control.

The Low Road argues that giving more control locally will create injustice, inequality, and a dangerous tribalism. Meanwhile, they will never explain how to stop outside elitism from usurping local consent. They will never explain how to inspire more local volunteerism or add more personal creation. They will never say that their intent is to abolish all forms of democracy.

Supporters of central control believe human beings are all self-seeking, so they have to manage our "self-centeredness" with authoritarianism. They don't believe we're born with any quality other than self-interest. They don't believe we can manage community together. They seek to usurp the very responsibilities that make people free.

To understand why some people believe as they do, let's begin with a fair look at the far right. The far right is not part of the Low Road and it's not an elitist class. The Low Road seeks to censor and control the far right. We must speak to the far right *first*, because it has the best chance of taking the High Road. The far right is higher up on the Citizen's Atlas than the far left.

The Far Right

If you're labeled "far right," what that means is that the far left, especially those on the low left, paint you as racist, bigoted, greedy, narrow-minded, homophobic, redneck, carnivore, and so on—you get the picture. The far right is labeled by all kinds of negative terms. Adherents of the far right are called selfish by those on the far left because they live mostly alone and for themselves. They don't harm anyone, but nor do they do little good unless placed under extreme authoritarian pressure to organize. It's important to understand that we aren't talking about the far right as described by those on the low left. We're talking about actual people on the far right, not about the labels heaped on them by those with curved intentions.

While the far right lives independently, none of the labels above are true. Contrary to cardboard-brown or linear thinking by those on the Low Road, the far right believes we are born with rights. That's why they tend toward constitutionalism and the rule of law. That isn't progressive; it's just barely sustainable. The far right is mostly concerned with the protection of rights, the rule of law, and the Constitution. Nothing can progress without protecting these.

Far-right adherents worship the Bill of Rights, perhaps more than they worship God. They believe in rugged individualism, but they never explain what that means or how it works. They stand for American Greatness, but they stress greatness for individual achievement and rarely the greatness of an entire people.

As a group, they will gladly stand hand-in-hand with an Asian gay man—as long as he supports the Constitution.

The far right says, "as long as I do no harm to others, don't tread on me." They live by a simple credo, "wrong no man, corrupt no woman, and defraud no child."

Far-right individuals keep to themselves. As a people, they don't organize very well. They avoid the social collective because they don't trust collectives. They trust rights bestowed by God—and, typically in that order: rights, then God.

Whether independent, libertarian, constitutionalist, patriot or fiscal conservative, none of these organize very well because they prefer individual rights over collective consent. The public and private organizations they do create are top-down and centrally controlled, just like those on the far left. The far right hates taxes, not because they have no voice, but because more taxes subtract from what they can keep.

What value the far right keeps is more important than having a voice in creating that value, and that's the Achilles' heel of the far right.

With patriotic fervor, adherents fight to keep their value, but they neglect to keep their voice. If they had all the power in the world, they would abolish most taxes, especially the property tax, which is the base tax for supporting local health, education, and welfare services. The far right will shoot itself in the foot before standing up for anything, and usually it stands up to defend its rights late in the game.

The far right has a place, though. It exists to keep us from falling to the low left. The far right will die to protect property, life, and liberty, usually in that order. Using the critical-thinking process discussed in the first part of this book, we can ask a series of questions about liberty to help understand the far right's limitations.

Is liberty an idea expressed in the Constitution? Is liberty a statue? A monument? Or is liberty an action? Remember when we talked about action being the pure working model for words like love, democracy, and hundreds of abstract nouns? Liberty is action, and when we define very important words as a clear action, we see the working meaning, and this is common sense.

For example, let's define liberty in action. Let's say *liberty is the hand that adds value.* Liberty here is seen as an act of creation. If acts of creation and adding value are inseparable from liberty, then how do we protect the people's ability to create and add value? In other words, how do we inspire others to add value and then protect the value that they create?

Answer this, and supporting liberty changes from a stagnant high-mindedness into the action of creating value. If we cannot protect value, we cannot protect creation, and creation is the greatest right we have.

The far right has neglected this approach. Adherents seek to secure their value as an inactive right tied to optional choices—and not the liberty of sharing an idea and protecting the creation that came from that idea. Calling American Greatness "individual rights protected by the Constitution" is just not good enough. Liberty is something the far right either has or wants to protect. They have it backward! Liberty is not the protection of something you have, it is the creation of value that you don't have.

For example, the creation of a better carburetor that emits no pollutants and uses less far less gas is not welcomed by Big Oil. There are many instances where a new idea competes with established technology or established power—and we never get to see the new idea. Atlas witnessed this first-hand when he lived in a spare room while attending graduate school. The owner of the home was Chuck Stamps, Sr., who in his home had several carburetors he'd invented that would get up to eighty miles per gallon. He had several patents on the wall and showed Atlas how the carburetors worked. For years after, Atlas could not understand why new cars got such low gas mileage. Even after many decades, we still manufacture cars that get the same low gas mileage.

Common sense says we should protect creation. We shouldn't engage in protection racketeering to favor those who already possess value. If there's a better value, we should protect and inspire the new-value creation.

American Greatness is creation. Protect the hand that adds value, and we inspire more creation. This is how liberty works, and it's also common sense.

Defining abstract words as active gets us closer to the working meaning. And the working meaning builds our common sense. By defining liberty as the hand that adds value, we connect the act of creation to the value produced. If the hand that adds value isn't our own, we are in a state of dependency. American Greatness doesn't function in a state of dependency. It functions in a state of creativity. Liberty is pure creation.

When we look at liberty honestly, it should bring value (new creation) and voice (ideas) together with the people's vote (their agency). Advancing the cause of liberty is about decentralizing the control of voice and value at great distances and returning them to people, locally, with their vote. The far right doesn't understand how to accomplish this because value typically in their eyes is held by individuals, not communities or regions.

The far right doesn't stand on the shoulders of the founders to see the power of liberty in people. At best, the far right remains at face-level by admiring the founders as great individuals rather than as people who worked together under great stress. The far right doesn't see the potential for greatness now. This lack of responsibility for greatness now must change if the far right hopes to survive.

The far right remains determined to hold positions of thought: "the right to free speech" or "the right to keep and bear arms." Meanwhile, its adherents don't organize effectively to create processes that secure liberty as an act of building a vibrant community, which is the greatest creation of all. They will *take charge* to fight against corruption, but they will not *take responsibility* to put better systems in place to protect everyone's creation. The far right is reactionary, remaining mostly isolated, alone, and independent until a major crisis threatens its rights. Even though its advocates stand by their belief that we are born with rights from God, they act too late to validate those rights.

Their procrastination in dealing with the low left is evidence of this. Far-right adherents will give their lives for the belief that we're born with certain inalienable rights, but they lack the understanding of how to build a greater America, and they shrug off the responsibility required to organize people. Without any depth of meaning, the far right appeals to the Constitution and capitalism, almost intermixing them as one.

Consider that the most powerful right is the right to peacefully assemble. All other rights are secondary. If we cannot peacefully organize to share voice together, we have no value in common.

The far right doesn't organize with full voice, vote, and value creation. At most, it shares memes that show a lack of common sense on the other side. All it has is a frustrated hope that the next election cycle will fix everything. Restoring the Constitution is the ethereal magic that will solve everything.

Far-right adherents have moved away from local caucuses where they had more voice and have adopted popular voting with no real exchange of voice. Why would the far right stand for this? Since they don't fight to protect voice in common, they don't fight to keep any real value in common. In fact, the far right holds no real value in common at all, and this is due to its love for capitalism as a kind of morality with no responsibility.

Here is where it gets touchy. The far right confuses capitalism with the free market. Capitalism is the protection and growth of capital. For example, you can buy real estate, or a business, that generates cash. With the profits from that business, you buy more stuff as a business expense. Then you pay no taxes on the first profits because they were categorized as an expense. The endless legal loopholes of capitalism changes liberty's focus from value creation to property protection, and it marks the beginning of the death of both liberty and value.

The goal is to accumulate more stuff that produces cash, and do this over and over until you have capitalized on your capital. Capitalism is like betting on a horse race.

However, in a free and fair market you can't move your bet from horse to horse during the race. You must place your bet before the race and wait to see who wins. With capitalism, you can move your capital from horse to horse during the race. We call this speculation, or trading.

Capitalism is not creation: it is the ability to acquire, control, and preserve capital. It's not evil, it's just not as profitable as liberty. Capitalism doesn't champion the cause of liberty (the hand that adds value), rather, it seeks to suppress or control the hand that adds value.

When the far right says capitalism is free enterprise, they are confusing the liberty to create with the freedom to capitalize on that creation. Capitalism thrives on creation; it is not creation.

The idea of capitalism as a grand right or liberty can only last until socialism, communism, or another form of totalitarianism takes over as a false promise to make things equal and fair. When that happens, the only good left in capitalism is competition. If you cannot control the entire market, a new idea in the market will surface. Unfortunately, competition is controlled by those with the most capital, so even competition isn't welcomed by capitalism.

The far right often fails to recognize capitalism's greatest fear, which is its hidden contempt for competition. They say capitalism promotes more competition, but it clearly does not. Competition threatens the survival of self-interest. Competition threatens established hierarchies, established wealth, and established markets. This focus on self-interest is the heart of capitalism, and it's what angers the far left.

The far left is correct to be concerned, but its adherents have no solution that protects the pure creation of liberty.

If capitalism is a far-right economy always at odds with the far left's need for equality, then free enterprise is a High-Road economy as long as it can protect the voice, vote, and value of those who are *creating* value.

Free enterprise wants to invent, improve, and add value. It's driven to produce and make something better even at great sacrifice and loss. But when capitalism seeks to control that value, it sees just far enough into the future to speculate a financial return on that value, even if it means shutting that value down.

Capitalism seeks to maintain its own competitive control by suppressing new value creation. Free enterprise has yet to figure out how to combat the ravages of competitive control. It is focused entirely on the hand that seeks to add value.

The best ideas never seem to advance because they threaten the established power that's in control. In other words, free enterprise has not figured out how to inspire more value creation without it being usurped, shut down, or bought out.

Those on the far right have little vision for anything that brings people together economically. They can't see the future, because they are focused too much on restoring the past. The far right's best quality is protecting us against the authoritarians on the low left and the low right. The far right stands for personal responsibility, but its adherents have no foresight for social responsibility. When it comes to the future, they have no dream.

But when it comes to war against a tyrant, they will happily give their lives.

We don't need to fight another revolution to restore speculative capitalism and stagnant individual rights. We still have time for a fresh start that could launch free and fair opportunities for all. A fresh start needs to find a way to conserve value creation in the hands of individuals and local communities that create that value. This inspires more value creation. The culture that solves this sets the foundation upon which we can build a new American renaissance. The failure to see this High Road is not just with the far right. We will equally blame the far left.

When someone uses the term "far right," it's often assumed to be synonymous with "uneducated, gun-toting, proud, patriot" and other similar ideas. Who would react to clichés that carry assumed meaning? Naming a list of stereotypes only reveals a fool.

If a female Catholic Democrat from Philadelphia genuinely tried to explain how an agnostic Republican man from Phoenix views the world, common sense ultimately demands that she ask him to explain himself until she gets it right. Labels and rumors distort reality because they don't come from the people they are describing; they come from the cardboard-brown of linear thinking, and often at a distance with no boots on the ground.

The Citizen's Atlas helps us see there are six fundamental sides in the political spectrum, not two. This six-part look at human thinking reveals why the High Road is unpopular with central authority because it rejects the assumption that we're stuck with a division that can never be resolved. The Citizen's Atlas is a way of organizing where left and right actually work together because they can finally see eye-to-eye on the High Road.

Let us now move to the far left to give balance to the far right.

The Far Left

The far left believes that we are born unequal. In the eyes of the far left, life is not fair. Its focus is on fixing inequality everywhere, and there is always inequality. The far left doesn't have the Constitution, a Bill of Rights, or any core principle to use as a focus. Injustice and inequality are core drivers. The far right's documents of liberty don't work for the far left, in part because they do not know them. These founding documents are not bad in the mind of the far left; they are just not enough.

The far left suffers from perpetual unhappiness, instability, frustration, and anger. Like the enterprising preacher that reminds the congregation of its sinful ways, the far left's leadership needs to accuse and blame. They genuinely see inequality everywhere, and because the far right is not openly bothered with inequality, the far left blames everything on them.

The problem with appearing apathetic to the far left, even if you are a genuinely caring person on the right, is that those on the far left see your inaction, or your difference, as proof of culpability.

Try attending just about any college or university in the United States as a conservative and you will feel the shame—and the blame—of holding different views. Because you don't see inequality as the primary evil in the world, you're perceived as insensitive ... and then conveniently blamed for everything. The great inequalities that exist are attributed to the entire right, and this includes the inequality of racism.

Even if most on the far right have done nothing to cause what they are blamed for, they are accused because they're not actively doing anything to solve inequality and racism. If they do try to solve an injustice somewhere, it's never big enough because those on the low left need constant blame to survive.

Here's the tragedy with the far left. Because they have no grounding that guides their thinking in taking responsibility, they work tirelessly to get control to force-fix the inequality. Their behavior tends toward more central control, and this attracts compromised and compliant people (grovelers, snivelers, and panderers). There is no alternate path for the far left than to get more control, because getting more control is the only solution it sees to fix inequality or any injustice. In order to get this control, the far left attracts a culture of compliance. Dr. Seuss (Theodore Geisel) described the far left in The Bee Watcher.

> Oh, the jobs people work at! Out west near Hawtch-Hawtch there's a Hawtch-Hawtcher bee watcher, his job is to watch. Is to keep both his eyes on the lazy town bee, a bee that is watched will work harder you see. So he watched and he watched, but in spite of his watch that bee didn't work any harder not mawtch. So then somebody said "Our old bee-watching man just isn't bee watching as hard as he can, he ought to be watched by another

Hawtch-Hawtcher! The thing that we need is a bee-watcher-watcher!" Well, the bee-watcher-watcher watched the bee-watcher. He didn't watch well so another Hawtch-Hawtcher had to come in as a watch-watcher-watcher! And now all the Hawtchers who live in Hawtch-Hawtch are watching on watch watcher watchering watch, watch watching the watcher who's watching that bee. You're not a Hawtch-Watcher you're lucky you see!

While the far right remains committed to the Bill of Rights and the Constitution (even while lacking concern for organizing for a greater good), the far left is typically deficient in core principles but highly adept at organizing. It's easier to organize concern than indifference.

Even though the far left focuses on fixing inequality, it doesn't trust the rule of law, the Constitution, or jurisprudence, unless it can control them. It seeks power, a new control model, or a regulatory body to fix inequality while blaming the right for those inequities.

The far left can organize effectively because it employs followers and flatterers seeking a position of importance.

The far left attracts followers because there's no responsibility required. Suppress enough voice and you advance yourself. Learn the rhetoric of the far left, repeat the doctrines, and hostility against you ceases. It assumes its noble ends justifies its controlling means.

The far left organizes naturally into bureaucracies, pure hierarchies of social protectionism. Adherents never create the equality they want because they have too many snitches and self-interested suck-ups in their ranks. This doesn't bother them, because they can still blame the right for all injustice and still remain in control.

A person on the far left has a deep hatred for anyone who disagrees with them. When the far left begins to attack character and personality, instead of cognition and principle, this begins their fall from greater idealism to the inevitability of low-minded hostility.

Essentially, unlike the far-right mindset that stands on the same core principle (not unlike a fence post stuck in frozen ground), the far-left mindset doesn't stand on any common-sense principle. Instead, it's always walking on thin ice that often collapses into truly cold waters. A far-left mind either realizes the path to the High Road, which is rare, or it trades free agency for control on the Low Road.

Inside the soul of a far-left mind is a demand for truth and answers. If adherents aren't educated to maintain freedom as their core driver, the cardboard-brown of curved intentions takes over. Such a mind cannot sit still and accept the status quo; it needs to constantly be trying to make things equal.

If adherents cannot find a way to make things equal, anger overwhelms them and soon they adopt the mind of the low left.

Summary of Far Minds

Neither the far left (that believes we are born not equal) nor the far right (that believes we are born with rights) will ever come together. Herein lies an essential problem. The two sides stand against each other in perpetual division because they fight to perpetuate flawed ways of thinking. Ideally, they should be mutually engaged in healthy, vibrant, and inspired self-discovery, but they aren't.

If we hope to launch a fresh start of American Greatness that's genuinely free and responsible, it cannot happen through those who believe we are born with rights, or through those who believe we are born not equal. Neither will scale to anything great, and they will never come together. If left alone, these divided beliefs will eventually destroy America and force a revolution. This will likely lead to the same powers behind the scenes picking up the pieces and establishing more control.

The far right and far left are not necessarily made up of bad people, they just cannot work together. They need help. Before we can give them a path to the High Road that is essential to their own survival, we need to unveil the schemer class of collusion found on the Low Road—the ones who fight for power even if it means enslaving the rest.

We'll look at the beliefs of these people momentarily, but there is one more thing about the far left and the far right we rarely discuss. They are quick to lose hope and make a trade for more power. Power is like dead roadkill. It attracts the wrong crowd.

The far left must kill hope to get power. Those on the far left never share this with new adopters of the belief that we are born unequal. A far-left mind is typically impatient and wants to see something happen that will make things equal. When nothing happens, their core belief shifts downward to something destructive, which is why we see more people on the far left sinking to lower means to achieve their curved intentions.

The same thing happens to the far right. If personal rights are ignored and abused no matter how much they quote the Constitution, people will stop thinking for themselves and cede their liberty to an authority that inevitably justifies more control, obscuring the truths they held so dear in the first place.

It is not good to remain in one mental place for too long. Every mind needs to be stretched and challenged, because either the mind becomes stiff in its need for control, or it adopts force or rigid fundamentalism (with the same need for control). Far left and far right minds have a hard time hearing new ideas, let alone opposite viewpoints.

And if we make the wrong turn down the path to the Low Road, we'll find some hideous places ...

The Low Right

The path on the Low Road is a dangerous route paved with authoritarianism. Those who take the Low Road approach it from either the left or the right. Each has a separate belief. However, both want the same thing: central control.

The low right has its roots in religious fundamentalism. Fundamentalism is a mind that stops. It stops at what it calls fundamentals, or a strict adherence to doctrines prescribed by an authority.

Fundamentalism imposes a mental lock that cannot move, think, or live outside of that lock. It's like living in an iron bubble. There are no higher truths to acquire in fundamentalism, no additional light or knowledge, and certainly no opportunity to share new ideas. State control and religious control have always dominated the Low Road. Until America arrived on the world scene, religious authority blanketed nearly every human institution. In fact, western history is the story of one religious power fighting another. Religious fundamentalism lost influence in most developed nations after the 16th-century Christian Reformation and the birth of representative government.

Some parts of the world still maintain religious fundamentalism that controls much of the local and regional culture. Iran is governed by religious fundamentalism. Islam is struggling with its own reformation. But while fundamentalism may still have a firm grip in the world, in the United States it remains in very small pockets, mostly dormant, isolated and outside the mainstream. The low left refuses to believe this because it diminishes their need to blame and shame the right, but it is true. The brain stop of fundamentalism has diminished significantly.

It could be fair to say that the low right has taken a slightly higher path by giving up its need for central religious control in exchange for God-given rights and the rule of law.

It's important to explain what the Low Road wants most before we reveal what the low right and the low left believe separately. Without a doubt, the Low Road wants control. Control is a false sense of power over something we never talk about. That something is death, including all symbolic connections to death.

There are many symbolic connections to death, including rejection, failure, hunger and starvation. Being judged by others is a representation of death. Bankruptcy can be a kind of death. Discrimination is like death. Racism can feel like death. The word death has many associated meanings that we falsely connect in our sub-conscious minds.

The Low Road is about controlling death, especially those stuck in the low right. Read the works of William James, Otto Rank, and Earnest Becker. If psychology and cultural anthropology are too thick to digest, read *Moby Dick* or Shakespeare. The need to control death can be traced throughout literature. It is not just a common theme, it's the engine for drama. In fact, one of the key ingredients to great literature is that it sustains a pressing sense of mortality. The low right and the low left are driven to control mortality, albeit differently for each side. Let's explain with a little more depth.

When a religious authority taps into any fear, that authority utilizes ways to control fear through any number of fastidious practices, rituals, or behaviors. These practices are meant to stop the mind from worrying. When those in religious power feed their personal solutions to people, a vast number will follow and obey in order to be accepted and live life without fear. Fundamentalism taps into the twin fears of rejection in life and physical death in order to control fear. Religious fundamentalism gets its power by controlling fear. Hype the fear, provide a solution to the fear, and you gain control.

We are now ready to see what the low right believes. The low right believes we are born sinners. This is their core belief, and it automatically puts fear in others. It also places everyone into an unfair situation where they are forced to accept what the authority says regarding our birth into sin. If we do not accept that we are born sinners, we must defy authority and suffer ridicule and rejection.

In other words, we are not born with an innate belief that we are sinners. Someone must teach this to us. Anyone who teaches that we are born sinners empowers themselves over the innocent. Sin is an indoctrinated belief. It is not an inherent idea fixed with the child from birth. Children do not grow up believing they are sinners. It is taught to them by adults with curved intentions.

Make no mistake, someone is sure to quote the Bible or some other text to prove that we are born sinners. For all we know, God himself believes that "... the imagination of man's heart is evil from his youth." The answer to this is simple, we can quote any source to justify our belief that we are born sinners. The real issue is that Americans will never achieve greatness with a belief like that. The belief that we are born sinners is not a lifting belief. It does not inspire, and it does not increase more love for others. It only gives power to the person who teaches it. And with this power they impose doctrines, practices, and rituals to control the innocent.

In other words, teaching that we are born sinners shuts down voice that might surface a better belief. Teaching that we are born sinners is un-American. It favors the idolatry for authority and not the self-discovery in each person's voice. Teaching that we are born sinners stops the mind, and this should be unacceptable.

The low right organizes easily because it controls fear. It tells us to submit and follow in order to be saved from rejection and death. Read Earnest Becker's *The Denial of Death*. Published in 1979, it won the Pulitzer Prize for general non-fiction. We have not had a writer since who has spoken with such honesty about a central motive in humanity that the low right has spent thousands of years using to control people.

The low right can draw in members from the far right because it feeds the need for solid and immovable truth, the kind of truth that can tell the mind to stop, think no more, and join us. Even though the low right has diminished much of its influence, the appeal is still powerful. It can give belonging and purpose. It can also destroy conscience. It's called the fundamentalist farce. The mind is seduced by a fundamental doctrine that makes sense, to some degree, and it causes the same mind to adopt total central control because that authority promises to uphold that doctrine.

The problem we have with the low right can be revealed in thousands of texts and historical records. It is easy to research because of its history and pervasiveness. Fundamentalism is an open book with hundreds of years of research. From war to the genocide of the unclean in the name of religion (and not the state), the record books are open. This is not the case with the low left. The record books for the low left are now being written because it is now in power. Its war and genocide are equally driven by the same thing, the need to control and eliminate the genetically inferior.

The Low Left

The low left has a particularly limiting belief. It believes that we are born selfish. Human beings are not sinners, they are selfish. This kind of belief has a different approach. Unlike the teaching that we are born in sin combined with a strict prescription loaded with fastidious practices for attaining salvation or Valhalla, the dogma that humanity is inherently selfish takes a more camouflaged approach.

Selfishness as a motive is hidden by the low left, and even adopted many times by the low right, as an innate character flaw in humanity. By drawing attention to a worthy societal affliction to be cured, the low left employs shame and guilt on others while achieving their secret goal of gaining more control. As they move to create more central control to achieve a good that the right is guilty for not causing, you can easily see the low left in action without knowing their true motive.

The father of low left thinking is Plato, the author of our modern-day destruction. We could go all the way back to Cain, the son of Adam. But Plato first published the thinking of the low left and formalized their organizational structure in *The Republic*.

The actual confusion began in Book One of *The Republic*, where Thrasymachus debates Socrates over the meaning of justice. Thrasymachus argues that "justice is the interest of the stronger." Socrates argues that "... no science or art considers or enjoins the interest of the stronger or superior, but only the interest of the subject and weaker."

Throughout the rest of *The Republic*, Plato took the logic of Thrasymachus and designed a model supporting the idea that justice is for the strong. By replacing seekers of power with benevolent philosopher-kings, Plato still has power centralized. This is the greatest failure the low left has adopted as its central design.

According to Plato, power is wise, good, and true, because we will always have the right person in power. This was his assumption derived from the cardboard-brown of linear thinking. Since Plato advocated for less voice from the people and more central control by so-called "philosopher leaders," *The Republic* has become a manual for despots and a bible for dictators.

The Republic is a wolf in sheep's clothing. It is not a republic at all. It is totalitarianism. Read Plato's *Republic* and ask one question: "How does Plato's republic work?" You won't find the answer. Plato never explained how a republic works. A low-left mind will never explain how its ideas work. Adherents just say their ideas are good, or they are the best, without explaining how.

The Republic is a book Mao would have read with pleasure— and he did, according to some reports. But it is a book Thomas Jefferson couldn't bear to read. While expressing concern for the people publicly, Mao tyrannically murdered over seventy million of his own people. Jefferson liberated an entire country by listing the abuses of a tyrant.

Plato argued for leaders to have wisdom, temperance, and courage, nebulous concepts that are impossible to measure without common sense and systems to prove them. Jefferson and the founding fathers argued that all men are created equal, and they drafted a social contract and created the best system they could at the time to protect the equality of the citizenry.

While the low left uses the argument that they are fixing injustice, inequality, or the newest crisis, they are quietly pushing for central control by one leader, a centralized unelected body, or the global elite. This is why they can attract those on the low right at the same time, the promise of getting central control is too tempting.

You can spot the low left as they install more regulation often outside the legislative process, more central control by appointed directors of agencies, more scarcity, and a corporate body funding the lobby arm that pushes the policy of more control. Over time the low left has learned to pander to great wealth, and now we have something never imagined, the rise of corporate communism.

When big tech works seamlessly to silence the entire right, we have collusion meant to centralize power for its benefit. The right is now deemed so bad that the left is forced to silence half the population to keep it from infecting the world. Sounds a lot like a purge and a cleansing at the same time!

Communism is nothing more than centralized power. Meanwhile, the dead-stream media promotes the entire narrative of more central control as the highest progressive model. What they say in public is not what they believe in private. This is the true form of selfishness.

Just look at the European Union. It's controlled by an unelected body that lives in lavishness and complete detachment from the people. The United Nations is controlled by appointed bureaucrats too afraid to say anything against the top-down compulsory groupthink.

BREXIT happened because the people of Great Britain lost their voice. The World Health Organization is run by just one person, a director general. The CDC is also controlled by one person who's controlled by private interests and not the public good. The United States is now inundated by dozens of intelligence agencies, each run by one person. These individuals are then controlled by power interests from outside the public voice, known as the deep state.

On and on, we see how the low left (and, in part, the low right) creates a leviathan of centralized control with constricted voice hiding behind the perception that they are making things equal, good, and fair, or that they are saving the planet.

One of their philosophers is Thomas Hobbes. In his *Leviathan*, Hobbes took on the Platonic mantle and favored a divine right of aristocracy. He argued for the need to obey power and authority at all costs, or suffer the consequences of continued revolutionary bloodshed. If not for strict obedience to a central authority, the "mutual relationship between protection and obedience" is severed. These are the words of a protection racketeer, a common theme among the low left.

If we are required to obey authority, what stops authority from taking more control?

The low left has used Plato, Hobbes, and others as their central texts because these authors don't explain how justice works, they only give justice a high-minded importance managed by appropriate leaders. In our day, the low left has morphed into the social justice movement, the woke culture, cancel shaming, and various philosophies that have given up the spirit of civil disobedience. They constantly say what justice is, but never explain how it works for everyone.

This is called elitism. It is the belief that ordinary men and women are too selfish to govern their own affairs, therefore force is justified.

Plato puts justice in the hands of leaders. Jefferson, Locke, Hamilton, Adams and others put justice in the hands of our peers. The founders explained how a republic worked and gave us a working model. Plato gave us a vertically integrated power structure with no voice from the common citizen, which means no transparent redress for any wrongs.

Thrasymachus may have been the first to derail Western thinking. In fact, he can be read as a foreshadowing of Nietzsche and Machiavelli, both of whom argued that power is the ultimate goal of leadership. This drive for power defines the low left perfectly. Thrasymachus is the first spokesperson for a cynical realism that "might makes right," or that we are all born selfish.

Friedrich Nietzsche, Niccolò Machiavelli, Thomas Hobbes, and other philosophers advocating for an all-powerful central state were followed by Marx and Engel's *Communist Manifesto*, George Orwell's *1984*, Aldous Huxley's *Brave New World*, and Ray Bradbury's *Fahrenheit 451*. Later we had movies like *Soylent Green*, *Logan's Run*, *The Hunger Games*, and dozens of others. Even Superman is the story of a child who escaped Krypton, a low-left authoritarian society in collapse.

Secret societies push for more central control, Saul Alinsky sows discord in the public for the same end, and the Cloward-Piven strategy destroys free markets in healthcare to favor the eugenics societies demanding control of all health and reproduction without your consent ... all this is low-left poison. While religious fundamentalism seeks to cleans the population of the unclean, low-left totalitarianism seeks to eliminate the genetically inferior.

Low-left thinking hasn't stopped; it's morphed into an élite class currently moving toward a breakaway civilization of its own. Because it believes all humans are born selfish—and therefore incapable of achieving anything powerful on their own—the low left seeks its own utopia of a unipolar world government.

In fact—and here's the most disturbing truth of all—the great murder rampage throughout the 1900s was committed largely by the low left, aided to some degree by low-right minds. The low left's main purpose is to centralize power at all costs and to profit secretly from it. That is the only way to logically manage all the selfishness in the world as an outward projection while secretly lining your own pockets. Try arguing that Mao was a religious zealot! You won't win that argument. He was a statist, with himself in total power. It is no surprise that many academics today worship Mao.

It's not surprising that the low left spends billions trying to blame crises and conflicts on the right, gaslighting citizens by blaming the far right to deflect attention from its selfish ambition for power.

On January 6th of 2021, the very day Congress convened to decide the electors for the presidency of the United States and hear all redress of grievances of voter fraud, questionable agitators coopted a peaceful rally to storm the capital. A woman inside the building died from a gunshot wound. The tragedy was entirely blamed on the right.

Within twenty-four hours the entire right was shamed by the media around the world. The low left used a focal event in which a small number of professional disrupters—with questionable ties to low-left backers—was used to redirect the nation's attention. This small mix of people included some professional disruptors and others duped by a PSYOP character named Q. These people entered the capital through doors opened by capital police from inside after some people in black masks had smashed windows with hammers. Meanwhile hundreds of thousands were outside expressing their voice in peace.

In fact, the break-in occurred roughly twenty minutes before the greater masses arrived, who were still listening to the president speak in front of the White House when the break-in occurred. Atlas was there. He witnessed hundreds of small groups sitting and standing in quiet prayer by the Washington Monument and in front of the White House, a stark contrast to those in masks edging the uninformed to storm the capital while others were screaming at the top of their lungs to stop those agitators and not enter the capital. None of this was reported by the dead-stream media, which had no presence on the ground. Everyone who attended the event was shamed by false association.

We cannot connect all the corruption in the modern world to low-right fundamentalism, when in fact it is low-left selfishness that's to blame. This isn't picking a side, it's speaking out. Low-right fundamentalism has had its day, unless the low-left gives it new birth by aligning with uncorrected fundamentalism.

We need to admit that the hidden selfishness of the low left, and the same need for power on the low right, both thrive on central control. Therefore, it makes sense for them to collude with each other wherever possible. The need for control is a serious illness, and when it organizes, it attracts the worst among us.

When a low-left person enters a room, they look for a power center to either collude with or dominate, making it clear why selfishness is a truly destructive mode that can only build one system for others to join—authoritarianism. Selfishness doesn't trust people; it trusts only itself. It doesn't trust a social contract, a constitution, or rule of law. It trusts the divine right of kings, just as long as the most selfish is the king.

In the process of securing a little fiefdom, a low-left mind first shuts down voice by (ironically) labeling those on the right selfish, irresponsible, hateful, irrational, racist, and lawless. It's called the "wrap-up" smear, actually taught and practiced by low left politicians. You smear somebody with a falsehood, you merchandise it, and have the media document it. You then can say "it's reported in the press" to give it validation. Now the press has reported the smear, and the magic effect is the wrap-up smear. Tell a lie, make it big, repeat it often, and the majority of people will believe you. It's one version of gaslighting.

Selfishness conditions others to believe they are selfish, as a way to deflect away from its own selfish motives—in other words, using projection.

The low left is expert at both gaslighting and projection. Call your opponent a racist or Nazis, and you hide the truth that you are precisely what you call others.

The low left trusts only itself. Allowing others to have equal voice is unacceptable; that would put its power at risk. The low left is worse than a self-imposed fundamentalist brain stop that does not allow new ideas to challenge its own authority. Instead, it's the deliberate suppression of a new idea. For instance, the low right may not let new ideas in their head, but low left minds will actively censor ideas from entering someone else's head. Any partnership is temporary, because seizing power is the low left's main drive.

When you see a low-left mind justifying censorship, limiting voice, or name-calling the right in negative terms while signaling its fake goodness, walk away. If it's hard to step away and stand on your own, perhaps a peek over the edge might help you distance yourself from the scheming classes on both the low right and the low left.

But be warned! Once you look into the abyss and down the path of the low road, you may become sick, but it's an important exercise if only to better recognize the greater importance of the High Road.

Dante's Pit

How deep does the low left and the low right go? Dante revealed the depth of hell in his classic poem The Inferno, in which he recounts a journey to the underworld. On the way down he describes several steps he calls "circles" that lead to the bottom. The first circle, or ledge, is especially important—it's "limbo," which is another name for neglect. This is a person who sits and watches what happens below, and eventually slides into lust, gluttony, greed, anger, and finally, at the bottom, treachery.

Treachery is the sowing of discord, the deliberate telling of a lie or the creation of a crisis while blaming someone else. Treachery is designed to create division and hatred that the sower of discord controls. The sower of discord creates the problem, everyone reacts in hysteria, and the same person who created the problem immediately offers a solution.

If you believe that all humans are born selfish, it's natural to engage in treachery to achieve your goal of total control. The low left is heavily engaged in treachery by calling everyone on the right a "racist" and "white supremacist," over and over, especially when a crisis comes.

The Emperor Nero displayed treachery when he capitalized on the great fire in 64 AD, which burned much of Rome. He blamed it on the Christians. Even if he did not start the fire (though many believe he did), he still used it to sow discord for his own gain. The sowing of discord never needs to be manufactured; any existing crisis will do. Just co-opt the emergency with a new control solution and frightened people will buy into it. Not everyone is selfish, but organizations can attract a significant number of adherents who are privately selfish.

You can spend decades studying and talking about treachery and never wake a small portion of the people, because sowing discord works in secret. This is the difference between the low right and the low left. Countless researchers, podcasters, and journalists have documented treachery from around the world, and it never seems to get into the mainstream because independent writers are derailed, or accused of being conspiracy theorists.

From human trafficking to the harvesting of child adrenochrome, the depth of corruption on both the low left and the low right reveals a darkness that compromises people in order to control them.

It's not absolute power that corrupts absolutely; it's power that attracts the corruptible. This is why the low left and the low right can organize so well; they appeal to base fears that are easily made to bend and obey. The low left demands control over selfishness to stop the destruction of the world by selfish people. The other side believes everyone is a sinner and seeks control to keep souls from committing sin.

The need to control was given birth before humanity began to organize. It started with two spirits in the heavens that proposed two choices. Notice the difference in these two spirits.

First spirit said,
Here I am, send me,
I will be the rescuer,
I will be your son,
I will fix all mankind,
and not one soul
will be lost. Give me
the honor.

Second spirit said,
Father, your will be done,
and the glory be yours
forever.

The first spirit proposed to take free agency away from humanity in order to rescue everyone from their self-destruction. This spirit believed that not one soul would be lost in exchange for all the glory. This is the low road, completely central control under one hand. Humanity has taken the low road several times when we believe human beings are born in sin or born selfish.

The second spirit doesn't take free agency from humanity. This spirit doesn't need glory. This spirit willingly gives everything to protect the self-discovery of human creation we call liberty. This is the High Road.

Before we can discuss the High Road, let's look at this need to control in more detail. It only takes a moment of looking into the pit of hell to gather sufficient knowledge. Don't look too long: it can take your life.

Let's be honest. In the United States, and in much of the diminishing free world, the low left has secured tremendous power—and the far right is only now waking up to it. Stalin's Bolshevism, for example, claimed to represent the majority. In a similar way, the low left also claims to represent the people, but it doesn't. It's the new oligarchy. The low left includes the great majority of Wall Street, the media, education, central banks, the entertainment industry, big tech, Washington, much of the health-care industry, and many state governments and corporations. Since the low left has so much control and power, why is it always talking about racism? Why does it ignite riots? Why the gaslighting and shaming those on the right?

The answer is simple: it's the best way to grab control.

Because the far right still holds to individual rights and personal freedom, the low left mistrusts and therefore hates these principles. The low left won't be happy until it abolishes everything it hates and gets the control it wants.

The low left has no vision other than total control. It is the same as the first spirit that said, "give me the honor and I will save humanity." It thinks it can fix everything as long as it has total freedom to control everything. Starting from the premise that all human beings are born selfish, there is no way anyone can have individual rights or personal freedom. The low left's crusade to suppress and ban the right will inevitably push the far right, and maybe some on the far left, to higher ground.

As things will get progressively worse under low-left control, we'd better study the fear and denial that motivates its adherents. The world isn't selfish, but it is fast becoming governed by people who believe it to be. They're not driven by a fundamentalist belief that human beings are born in sin; they're driven by the belief that human beings are born selfish. The first is a false religious dogma; the second is satanic and worships the underworld as the supreme expression of selfishness.

Fear and Denial

It's hard to believe that people can be compromised and made compliant enough to follow even the most hideous actions. The reason is because of fear.

Study Communist China during Mao's reign and it's easy to see murder carried out by a controlling person telling the poor and hungry the cause of their starvation is a certain segment of the population, like farmers and landowners. These farmers and landowners then become a threat to the ecosystem of power.

If fear can be co-opted to cause one part of the population to destroy another, anyone can be made to follow dark actions against their fellow citizens, especially if put under the right pressure or the right programming. We have witnessed it happening in Russia, Germany, Cambodia, the United States—and around the world.

To understand how powerful fear can be as a motivator, we can examine seven major "preoccupations." Based on the fear, actions can be used to deny fear.

We've already seen how action is the best way to reveal the meaning of an abstract word like liberty, so let's apply that to fear. Fear is seen in the actions that surface from the feeling. We either accept what we fear through an act of love and faith (which are actions themselves), or we deny fear—also through actions. If we choose neither an action of acceptance nor an action of denial, all that's left is disability, that mental state where a person feels the fear directly with no valve to release it in acceptance and no means of escape it in denial. The experience of fear is unable to move in either direction.

The actions of denial are varied but not difficult to understand because they are common to our internal sense if not common knowledge. For example, one person may use vain ambition to repress fear, while another may use forceful rule. Human prejudice surfaces in one person while a desire for sex with minors shows up in another. The denial of fear manifests in action, just as love manifests in action. The book *Then Comes Heaven*, which will follow this book, spells out the actions of fear in more detail along with solutions to overcome them.

It would be wise for society to learn the dynamics of denial and make them a core teaching. We could make selfish motives on the low left and indoctrination of sin on the low right more transparent. Neither side wants you to know that sin and selfishness can be overcome and even entirely removed from culture and community. We're going to be challenged in the near future, but we can grab hold of the High Road: it will be the only way out of what will otherwise be a nightmare scenario.

Seven Preoccupations of Fear
Seven Ways of Darkness

Magical Powers	Vain Ambitions	Human Prejudice	Forceful Rule	Sexual Fixation	Material Attraction	Blood Letting
Fantasizes Personal Magic	Obedience to Worldly Things	Being of a Superior Race	Seeking for High Position	Justifying Sex with Many	Seeking to Possess Property	Murder and Genocide

The low right and the low left are stuck in denial. They attract people needing to bury their fear of life and their fear of death under various actions of justified denial. The low road is trapped inside the seven preoccupations of fear.

Feed the fear or the selfishness with a defensible denial (as seen in one of these preoccupations), and you gain allegiance. Convince potential followers on the far left that everyone on the right is selfish and a fascist, and suddenly you are justified in any action against humanity. This is what American Greatness is up against, a Low Road fueled by fear and imprisoned by denial.

How do we know this?

Take for example pedophilia and the human trafficking of children, kept hidden for decades in many countries by both the low left and the low right. From big government to big media, and from centralized religion to big-money elites and the entertainment industry, human trafficking has been used to compromise and control. Spend ten years in Hollywood, as Atlas has, and you quickly see the underbelly of compromised souls willing to give a pound of freedom for an ounce of status.

It's safe to say that the FBI, the NSA, and other government agencies are working more to hide corruption than reveal it. Independent journalists have risked everything to disclose the truth while those agencies remain quiet and complicit. When anyone discloses the truth, they are showdown-banned by big tech, shamed by the media, and ignored by elected officials. Independent journalists are even harassed by government agencies sworn to protect the most innocent of lives.

Fear can never be eliminated. It can only be repressed or accepted. If we repress fear, it surfaces in one of the seven preoccupations of denial above. The low left, and to some degree the low right, gathers people who suffer from one of these preoccupations; it's how they get compliant followers. If we accept fear, we move onto the High Road.

The seven preoccupations showcase seven actions that are used to deny fear. In *Then Comes Heaven*, a book to inspire a renaissance, seven actions of faith will be found to help us overcome the seven preoccupations of denial. In the forecasted book to follow, old men and old women dream dreams again. A fresh start with a new and everlasting heaven on earth pangs to be delivered. Sadly, it may take extreme challenges for many people to see a better way.

Authoritarian religious control and authoritarian state control are birds of a feather. When—and if—they align, you can bet they'll represent a formidable threat to the creative drive that is our liberty. Even without this alignment, the battle lines in America have been drawn between the far right and the low left. This is where America exists today.

We are split between individuals demanding rights without effective organization and a collective acting-out of selfish motives hidden among the seven forms of denial outlined in the illustration above—which the low left calls "diversity." The far right is going to lose this battle. Even though it outnumbers the low left, the far right is ineffectively prepared to fight a false ideal masking a dark motive.

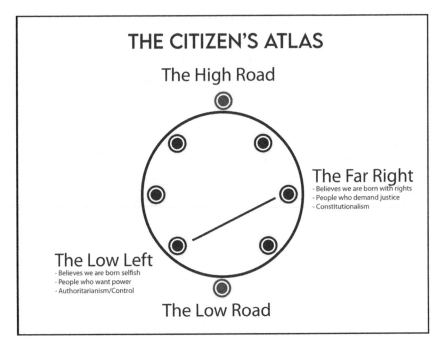

THE CITIZEN'S ATLAS

The High Road

The Far Right
- Believes we are born with rights
- People who demand justice
- Constitutionalism

The Low Left
- Believes we are born selfish
- People who want power
- Authoritarianism/Control

The Low Road

The liberty movement, as it currently exists on the far right, will fail against the treachery of the low left. Why? Because the liberty movement is no match for the highly organized low left working in secret. The liberty movement today looks to the past, at individual rights disappearing, rather than forward to social responsibility where we find the value in creation.

Another reason the far right will fail is because the far left is controlled by the low left's virtue signaling on every issue, which redirects the concept of selfishness onto the entire right. If the far right hasn't yet learned to battle this redirection, it will only get worse. Those who love freedom will be forced to organize a greater liberty that will solve inequality issues on the far left while protecting individual rights on the far right. Vision of this magnitude isn't impossible—in fact, it's necessary. It needs to be this powerful if it hopes to stop the global threat the low left is pushing for—total corporate collusion for power in bed with eugenicists and in part the last remnants of the fundamentalist low right.

Sooner or later, we will find this liberty in those who dare to take the High Road. Let's shoot for sooner rather than later. A fresh start is always better than a bloody revolution.

The High Good

The High Road is the path least traveled. As Shakespeare writes, "The evil that men do lives after them, the good often rots in their bones." We too often remember the bad, and don't see what is good. Even more, we too easily look to the past to see the good we lost, rather visualizing a greater good in the future.

The intelligent mind objects: restoring any vision for good only means it will get taken away again, as it was before. History repeats itself. We build something and lose it, then we rebuild something and then lose it again. Maybe it's time to build something good that's different from before.

Maybe it is time to build something everlasting.

The High Road is easy to forget because it isn't meant for the lonely traveler. The High Road exists for people to take *together*. This is one of the best-kept secrets of American Greatness; we are at our best as a people when times are at their worst.

The first belief that sets us on the path to the High Road is that we are born good. The second belief is that we are born free. Neither can stand alone. They are twin siblings of each other, almost conjoined at birth. We could say they share the same heart and that any attempt to surgically separate them ends in the death of both. If you can see this to be true, you have made the first step on the path to the High Road.

The high good (or the high right) believes we are born good. The high free (or the high left) believes we are born free. We use the qualifying term "high" for each because the High Road eventually brings them together as one. We call this coming together American Greatness. Freedom and goodness must come together if we hope to have a fresh start.

The *high good* is a kind of individual and community conservatism that protects each person's creative value within reach of the closest possible body. The *high free* is a kind of classical liberalism that protects each person's free agency. If these terms confuse you, stick with *good* and *free*. We need to move away from left and right terminology, because "left" and "right" are not complementary due to their divisive contexts. "Free" and "good," on the other hand, are mutually supportive.

If you believe we are born good, never debate with anyone who believes we are born sinners; it's non-productive and a waste of time. They have no vision for greater good; they're stuck in the rut of religious fundamentalism or that of state authoritarian control.

Instead, we should debate the value in what is good. For example, what is the effect on others when we believe we are born good? And who is *empowered* when we believe we are born good?

The belief that we are born good lifts others just as an incoming tide lifts all boats. The power in believing we are born good is not held by any authority over us; it's held within us. This is the big difference between believing we are born good and believing we are born sinners. Having a lifting power within us is far more beneficial than letting someone else tell us we aren't good! Religious indulgences (payments "guaranteeing" access to heaven) disappeared when we replaced the belief of our sinful state with talking to God on our own. The future of American Greatness is empowered by this same lifting belief within, not by an authority telling us what to believe.

The belief that we are born good focuses on family, friends, and community, often considered to be interdependent, especially the further you take the High Road. This is what Jefferson called true democracy "... the business ... of nearest and daily concern."[2]

Imagine not having a voice, or any local protection of value? That's the problem we have in America—we have lost teeth in our daily concern. We have lost true democracy on a local level and it has continued all the way to states and the nation, where our representative republic has been taken over by a ruling élite now in control of a compliant bureaucracy of followers and flatterers.

It all began when we stopped believing we are born good.

Those who believe we are born good seek to do good. They are the service-driven people in our communities. They give more than they take. If someone is in need, the good are typically the first to offer all they can. They give the shirt off their back. At a buffet, they are last in line. They are people who give as a labor of love.

In Victor Hugo's *Les Misérables*, Bishop Myriel is pure good. He stops Valjean from arrest and asks him to promise to live his life as an honest man, which Valjean does by becoming good. In other words, he exercised his liberty to add value and he was gifted with enough to start a new life. He then learned to conserve that value for those he loved, for those he employed, and for the larger community.

---

[2] Jefferson, Thomas. The Complete Works of Thomas Jefferson. Vol. 15. Page 70.

The nature of a good person is to add value, and too often they give with no protection of that value. Their credo is "do the right thing." Compare that to "wrong no man, corrupt no woman, and defraud no child." There is a big difference between *doing good* and *do no wrong.* The high good adds value. The far right, the far left, and all those on the Low Road, do not.

Those who take the Low Road eventually fall into a pit of darkness because they see no path other than taking more control. Those who take the High Road have the potential to reach a greatness in liberty rarely imagined in human history, because they see a need for more consent.

Control or consent, this is the true battle in America. We must choose more control or greater consent. The far right cannot take the High Road alone: it's exposed to too much risk in an imperfect system always scheming to get control of its value. The far left is equally exposed to the seduction of the Low Road where more control falsely promises equality—but with no consent.

Those who take the Low Road don't work alone. They gather suck-ups and snivelers, feasting on weak-minded fears compliant to the idolatry for authority. The Low Road commands an army of useful pawns, some of whom believe blindly until they learn the truth—and then become cynical. They live the rest of their lives doing neither good nor bad. They eventually die under a cloud of uninformed apprehension over what could have been their life's creation.

The Low Road burns through people fast, like a poorly run company with high turnover. The initial attraction gives followers a sense of belonging—until they recognize they have no voice and no incentive to add any value. A person is left with two options: shut up and live the balance of life in silence and fear, or drink the zealot's Kool Aid and accept the fruitless belief that human beings are born selfish and ripe with sin.

If individuals from the High Road work alone, they can experience the same discouragement. They can begin to see the world filled with takers, and all the good they give has no protection. The High Road requires greater effort to protect the two minds that define American Greatness, those who believe we are born good and those who believe we are born free. Great leaders in the future will focus on this challenge. They will see new vision in consent, and turn against more demands for central control. They will unite good and free souls together.

The high good and the high free need each other.

Throughout history, when we've organized, we've tended to elect a president or some central executive, a king, a chairman, a prophet, or some kind of number-one. Our worship of authority has gotten in the way of effectively working together for a vision that is good and free. Our idolatry of authority attracts gullible people compliant and easy to compromise. These lemmings get in power and keep good and free people out of the box where decisions are made. The good and free are then forced to work alone and with no control over the value they create.

The high good add value. Creating value fits perfectly with the true spirit of liberty as being the hand that adds value. Imagine a freshwater lake emptying into a saltwater lake. All the freshwater lake's nutrients and life die when added to saltwater. When value is wasted or lost, the incentive to add more value diminishes significantly. The high good cannot protect its freshwater alone. It needs help.

Even with all the value in the world to offer, the good cannot give their value until the conservation of responsibility is put in place. This means we need to find a way to keep the value created *in the hands that add that value.* Contrary to low-left thinking, this isn't selfishness" it's conservation, it's pure sustainability. The high good doesn't see how to protect or conserve value alone. These people need help from the high free.

If good and free people come together, we'll become the greatest force for liberty the world has never seen. This can only happen if we can organize our desire for good and our need to be free in a decentralized and headless way. This means we need to create more voice directly connected to a vote. It's the only way to give individuals and their communities real teeth in their value.

Before we can tackle this great challenge, we need to understand the importance of the high free. Like a long-lost twin brother or twin sister, they've been forgotten because they were separated at birth many years ago. They've been orphans long enough.

The High Free

John Stewart Mill wasn't perfect, but he did say one perfect thing. In the *Essay on Liberty*, he wrote, "The silencing of discussion is an assumption of infallibility."

While individuals are fallible, we are rarely fallible as a people, provided we do not silence discussion. In other words, conscience needs an outlet. It needs to ask questions and express ideas. The high left (which we define as the high free) has a mission to find the truth, and it maintains the core belief that humans are born free.

It doesn't matter whether or not this belief is true. The effect of believing we are born free is that it makes for a better world.

Freedom almost guarantees that those who believe we are free will find the truth in time. If it takes a generation, they will find it—even if they aren't free. The need to find the truth is a personal drive that freedom cannot ignore.

While the far right is open about what it *thinks* but closed to what it will *hear*, the far left (because they are now intimidated by the low left), is closed to thinking.

The high free, in contrast, are open in both ways. They are open about what they think *and* open to new ideas. The high free is classically liberal (which is almost extinct). The extinction of the high free is almost proof enough that the low left is in control today.

If we were dominated by low-right fundamentalist religious control, the classical liberal advocating for freedom would surface naturally. That person does not speak up today because the far right has taken up their cause.

In other words, if a classical liberal speaks up, they fear shaming because they would sound like a far-right person talking about liberty, the equal application of the law, rights, and the constitution.

It's time for a classically free-minded person to take up the cause of a greater liberty, something that's even greater than what the far right talk about. When the high free does this, more will follow and the path to the High Road will become the dominant road.

The difference between believing we are born free and believing we are born not equal is monstrous. Likewise, the difference between believing we are born good (the high right) and believing we are born with rights (the far right) causes a huge shift in the way we interact with each other.

That shift means we'll be exercising greater responsibility as a community.

Responsibility is the most precious quality in American Greatness. The far left wants to take responsibility away from local and individual hands and reorganize under central control. Linear thinking assumes if we centralize authority, we can make life equal for all. Just above them the high free want to make sure responsibility is never taken away, but sadly they have lost their original gift for freedom. The only reason people fall from a belief that we're born free to believing we're born not equal is that they see too many people not willing to take responsibility.

If a mind sees a growing lack of responsibility and nothing else, it assumes society is best managed by the few responsible ones in central control. The far left too easily loses faith in freedom and they adopt the belief that we are born selfish, which means more control. The belief that we're born not equal never lasts because it eventually collapses into the belief that we're born selfish. The far left seems to take the low road much faster and easier than does the far right.

The moment a mind changes its belief from "we are free" to "we are not equal," the classical liberal becomes an inequality hound and begins blaming everyone on the right. All this happens because they lose hope in humanity, which means they lose faith in freedom.

The best hope the free mind has is to join with the good. The community and family-focused strength of the high good will always believe in doing good. If you have not figured it out, the conservative who is driven to add value keeps the liberal from falling to centralized state authoritarianism. And the free liberal keeps the good conservative from falling into fundamentalism and a mental brain stop. Both authoritarianism and fundamentalism are destructive, and if they accomplish their goal to be unified as one, we will see the two merge into the idolatrous worship of an underworld terror that hates life and humanity.

The high free's secret is that they always have a working mind. They never stop thinking, and that's exactly what the conservative needs: constant and vigorous discussion. If not, they stop thinking and fall prey to singular fundamentalist ideas. They may take a stand on a few truths, but eventually their mind gets stuck inside an iron bubble.

The conservative right, overall, is more focused on practicality, making sure good is done and things work at their best. They will hold to strong ideas and principles that have been proven good for many years, but without the free liberal they can lose hope and fall into stagnancy and fundamentalism.

As the good keep their hearts pumping for virtuous action, the free keep their minds seeking truth. Together, when they work for a common vision, they manifest American Greatness. The high free and the high good create the perfect union. The only problem is that the free mind has walked away from its roots and the far right has lost the vision of anything greater than individual responsibility.

To make matters worse, in academia no one can be a classical liberal anymore, and certainly not a genuine conservative who wants to protect what is good. Too much free openness and good action favor a critical mind. This doesn't agree with modern correctness and cancel culture in which you can longer hold any truths or support wide-spectrum freedom.

Still, there is hope on and for the High Road. This hope can only be imagined if we keep two core beliefs alive: that we are born free and that we are born good.

Sticking together to reignite these two beliefs is our only salvation. It's accomplished by working together to preserve the voice, vote and value in each person, in each family, and in each community and beyond, and do it in that order.

Remember what we said earlier about the three types of leaders? Those who take control, those who take charge, and those who take responsibility? Setting up a compliant bureaucracy doesn't set up a system that protects the voice, vote, and value of all. Those who take responsibility set up systems and processes for others to use—without sacrificing their voice or their value. Great leaders in the future will guide their actions in this way, and this new statesmanship will have resources. The founding works of thought to launch this new renaissance will be called forth. We have only begun seeing the coming renaissance that will be born of our current crises.

Taking charge requires dependency on a person in charge, and this isn't a lasting approach. Those who take control assume all power under their command and tell everyone what to do, with no system in place to protect the free and the good. This latter type of leader collects compliant, non-thinking people.

We've had enough of that.

Free minds know the differences between leaders. They are always sensitive to the potential loss of their freedom, and are focused on creating systems that protect everyone's freedom. The biggest mistake free minds make is listening to low-left lies about the other side focused on doing good. As long as they cannot *see* good, it is easy to believe human beings are born selfish.

Because the good can easily align with free minds (using a process of greater democratic consent), free minds will organize with good people because it's the best way to protect free expression and open discourse. They can easily agree with each other without losing their unique core. They come together under the banner "freedom to do good." Together they create the working models for securing the kind of liberty the far right fails to protect as well as the vision the far left has lost under the pressure of low-left shaming.

While the high good keeps the high free from deteriorating into statism, the high free keeps the high good from deteriorating into fundamentalism. Together they encourage each other to focus on the "business ... of nearest and daily concern."

The minute the far left gives up the fight for equality and goes after more control for its own sake, it gives up any hope of achieving a better ideal. Unlike the far right—that can stay in the same place and hold to the same core principles for life—the far left needs to see something resembling progress. It needs to see life get better—even if that's done by shaming and force. When it chooses to shame or force its ideal on others, it falls into something truly destructive—the low left.

The only thing both the good and the free are missing is a system to integrate voice with a vote for everyone. Once they figure this out, the far right and the far left will take the High Road together. They will eliminate the attraction of compliant people who can be controlled, and they will, in time, eliminate central control everywhere it works best to do so. With a united front, they become a rising tide that lifts the far right *and* the far left to higher ground.

The proper marriage of voice and vote will be the secret that protects the free and the good. Together they will find truth and build communities and culture that will advance American Greatness beyond anything we can imagine. In fact, nothing will be withheld from them that they have an imagination to do. They will be one people. The future of American Greatness is at hand. *Then Comes Heaven* will explore that vision, plus something else now in the works that will solve the debate between the *Federalist Papers* and the *Anti-Federalist Papers*. It is called *The Community Papers*. The spirit of Atlas calls on all great minds to come together and write a founding book of papers for our time. For those interested, reach out to the author of this book. A grand convention of communities must convene, not to centralize but to decentralize and better organize themselves to attract value from every neighborhood. The Future of American Greatness is 100% local.

The Pillars of American Greatness

Pillar I: How Does That Work?
The first pillar of American Greatness asks *how* things work; not *what* things are. Asking how things work empowers everyone, while asking what things are emboldens authority. When we see how things work, we connect the dots on our own; we see a working example. When we're told what something is, we are at the mercy of the person telling us. To know how things work surfaces questions about each step. We should get back to asking how things work. American Greatness never defaults to an authority telling us what things are. It demands to know how things work, the true spirit of a classically conservative mind.

Pillar I:, Combine Voice, Vote, and Value Locally
The second pillar of American Greatness is the interconnection of voice, vote, and value. We will find ways to unite them and fight to keep them together. We will organize peacefully to keep them together in individuals and groups. People will move in the direction of common consent and work in modular form (small groups) to bring this unique trinity together. Eventually we will give up our desire for executives, presidents, and central authorities.

The future ahead of us will employ the tools of private coop-
eratives and trusts held in common by cultures of consent. These
can be scaled up, even though many will fight it. Greater levels of
social and cultural consent will be the focus of a second American foundation in liberty. Start thinking about how voice can
be incorporated everywhere, and then begin connecting voice
to a vote. Fight hard to keep them together! The rest will follow,
including the protection of value in the hands that add value, the
true spirit of a liberal mind.

Pillar II: Believe That We are Born Free and Good
The third pillar of American Greatness is that we are born good
and free. Believe this with all your heart. If you cannot believe
both, believe at least one. If we forget either one, we will give up
the spirit of high vision and lose sight of the heaven on earth we
are destined to establish. Every effort should be made to protect
the belief that we are born good and born free. These beliefs will
be the foundation for establishing heaven in America and then on
earth.

Some may still believe we aren't equal, and others may hold
fast that we are born with rights. There is nothing wrong with
these beliefs. But we cannot accept that we are born selfish or that
we are born in sin. Those who promote these low-road beliefs are
pushing the cause of darkness, not the cause of liberty. Correct
them and walk away.

They will either see the light or they will be left alone with
nobody to control.

Amen
Atlas is a true story of one life and many generations. For the
rest of us, our challenge is to unite two beliefs (we are free, and

we are good). This is the beginning of our renaissance. We are about to do what no people on earth have done on a grand scale, the perfection of a trinity for humanity, the integration of voice, vote, and value decentralized into democratic processes that take back "... the business ... of nearest and daily concern."[3] Now that we know the vision, we can begin to experiment again. Let our self-discovery guide us!

The path to the low road and its underworld of collusion for central control will overwhelm much of our freedom. It will impose force and create scarcity and even push for more division to increase that control. The true war of ideas is on. The greater the control imposed by the low road, the closer we get to the day when our need for freedom will be starved for a better way. When that day comes, those with the vision will be ready to plant in the hearts of many the true creative energy we call liberty.

Eventually we will bind in chains that serpent that has robbed us of our potential for thousands of years. It will not be easy, and it may take a generation to accomplish. We may even be forced to endure great tribulation, but it will happen as it was prophesied thousands of years ago:

> Seventy weeks are determined upon thy holy people and upon they holy city, to finish the transgression, and to make an end of sin, and to make reconciliation for inequity, and to bring in everlasting righteousness, and to seal up the vision and prophecy, and to anoint the most holy.
> (Daniel 9:24)

---

[3]Ibid

American Greatness will surface first in smaller and independent groups and private organizations detached from the mechanics of controlling systems. From very humble beginnings, it will eventually fill the earth as waters cover the sea.

A renaissance will begin in America and a very small elect in the United States will make an end of sin and bring in everlasting righteousness. This grand achievement may include immigrants from outside the country, as well as citizens within. We need to be prepared for a dynamic mix of people because the low left is selfish and controlling. It will dissolve borders in order to attract immigrants from around the world. Its intent is power, and if it can bring in as many uninformed into the United States as possible in order to grab more power in votes without any equity in voice, that's what it will do.

The United States is the target. Control this country, and the rest of the world is easy. This is why we cannot think in terms of fighting to secure the borders, personal rights, the First and Second Amendments, our Constitution, and so on. Those trying to escape the coming crisis by moving to the hills, as we see with the far right, won't be able to endure the coming crisis alone. The stuff being organized by the low left is too much for one person or one family to endure. We will need more help. We will need a greater community; one we create together.

This new renaissance won't be achieved by doomsday prophets, but by those who dare to take the High Road. The far right and the far left will join the High Road because they will see there is no other way to defeat the growing monster that tells people they will own nothing and be happy.

(Think about it. This means we will have no voice and supposably we will be happy. We will have no community and we will be happy. It's a diabolical lie and the true philosophy of the low road, the march to central control that can only be defeated by cultures of consent.).

The kingdom of heaven is at hand, and it is within us. It is not a unipolar world order hellbent on a post-human era where humanity is an afterthought. It's heaven on earth, the creative liberty of independent communities thriving on their own and connected to other communities with full consent. Like infinite points of light reflecting back into the universe, they will give hope to the great sacrifice of one Son.

And in the name of that Son, Amen.

Made in the USA
Las Vegas, NV
28 April 2021